Hanging by a Thread:

The History, Science, Technology and Culture of Rock Climbing and Mountaineering

Mark Reeves

DEDICATION

This book is dedicate to my parents, without whom none of this would be possible.

However a debt of gratitude is also owed to the great men and women of this world who not only pioneered new routes and climbing technology, but also the scientist, inventors and business men who have pushed forward the frontiers of technology. I hope you see this book as much a celebration of them and what they have achieved.

CONTENTS

ACKNOWLEDGMENTS

In writing this book I have spent too many hours in front of a computer, TV and books researching the stories contained within. I have shared many of the stories with many of my friends as the book has taken shape. In return they have also guided me to other stories that have added to the book. There are too many to mention and the stories were often recalled late at night in the Heights when bleary eyed and blathering. As such who told what stories when is something that is impossible credit.

However there is one person without whom this book would have been one long, complex and confusing stream of consciousness. Sue my editor has done an amazing job of reining me in and making me focus on what I wanted to say rather than go off on too big a tangent.

INTRODUCTION

This book is a brief history of climbing achievement set against the context of the technological advances of the human race. Whilst the footsteps of mountaineers are well documented in numerous books they are often set in isolation. By blending the history of human endeavour with that of climbers, a richer understanding of the tapestry of mountaineering unfolds. Going further than landmark ascents, a focus on the technology and scientific understanding of the time occasionally challenges the conventional wisdom in both climbing and scientific worlds.

In taking the threads of history from several diverse areas, and weaving them together we find patterns that echo down through time and lead us to the present. The book represents my love of rock climbing and passion for understanding the world around me. How I came to write this book then comes down to my own unique history.

My love of technology started when I was only a toddler, with a television that had buttons that needed the lightest of touches rather than pushing to operate the channels. A few years later these were obsolete with the birth of a remote control. This meant that my parents would no longer have to order one of their children to go to the TV and channel hop. Whether I am a digital native or immigrant I am unsure. My first TV had analogue tuning, but by the age of five I had come face to face with a brave new world of home computing in the form of Sir Clive Sinclair's ZX80.

This machine was the first low budget home computer; it had 4k of memory and the speed of a brontosaurus. If you are not very techy that means it would not be capable of opening the first chapter of this book as a text file. This early computer was my first introduction to computer code. In order to play any games required copying verbatim pages of incomprehensible letters and numbers. It was however an effort to educate people into the world of the BASIC computer language, made even more frustrating by the 'educational' mistakes the books were riddled with that the programmer had to solve.

My need to know how things worked was something of a problem to my parents who not only had to find answer to my incessant questions, but also deal with the fall out after I found the toolset and tried to 'repair' my toys and gadgets. Although none of the destructive talent came close to the one experiment I ran one afternoon after school, in my bedroom. The equipment needed to conduct this investigation into conductivity requires a knife, a plug and an electric socket. Start with the socket turned off, insert the plug and carefully push the knife in behind the plug, being careful not to touch any of the pins, and then turn the socket on. If nothing happens, put on shoes (preferably rubber soled) and hit the knife down with a plastic toy. Hide the knife that is now sporting two arc welds, and play dumb when your dad asks what shorted out the house.

To stem my destructive tendencies and nurture my thirst for knowledge, the investment made by my parents in a complete set of the Encyclopaedia Britannica[1], helped

---

1 The Encyclopaedia Britannica was what you needed to research a topic if you weren't in a library. A library (for all those children too young to know) was a place that students and old people went to read and be quiet before Tim Berners-Lee invented those four letters http (Hyper Text Transfer Protocol), on Christmas Day 1990. In launching the Internet the

develop my love of science. For a while I became obsessed with those many volumes, searching out factoids on science and history, somehow never managing to make the connection between that knowledge and the world around me. I attribute this to a lack of focus, which academically meant I was somewhat of a mixed achiever, excelling in the subjects that sparked my curiosity and failing those that did not. I was not a bad student, but from my early years I had one passion that has stayed with me throughout my adult life, an unwavering love for the great outdoors.

My passion for exploration and adventure started when I was just one year old, the day before my first family holiday to Cornwall. It involved climbing up a stack of suitcases in the spare room, and promptly falling out of the open window. I fractured several bones including my skull. Whether this highlights some 'instinct' within infants to climb, or that I was just a terror of a child is debatable. It made my den building, tree climbing and exploring the green fields and coppiced woodlands around my parents' home in Kent, seem a somewhat tamer introduction to the

---

brave new world of the information age was followed nearly ten years later by Jimmy Wales and Larry Sanger who started Wikipedia. However even they did not invent the concept of an open-source wiki. It was instead Ward Cunningham who wrote the code, but Jimmy Wales in particular is the most famous of all these people due to being the figurehead of Wikipedia. The Encyclopaedia Britannica became somewhat redundant in light of this free alternative, and in March 2012 it ceased to be available in printed format. Although Wikipedia users beware, it has a bias towards majority opinion on a subject, so if a recent piece of research has unearthed a re-evaluation of historical understanding, but it stands alone, then the conventional wisdom is followed rather than the truth.

great outdoors. Interestingly in India there is a baby dropping ritual that is meant to help develop the strength and vitality of the young child[2]. In it infants are dropped from a 15m high tower into a blanket.

By the age of ten I had grown to walking with a friend along the North Downs Way, an ancient pilgrimage route for Christians heading to Canterbury Cathedral. It was a big wide and unexplored world to me. You may ask what a parent was doing letting their 10 year old son walk unaccompanied by an adult across the countryside but back then the word paedophile was practically unheard of, as was the media scare mongering, as statistically a child is more likely to die in a traffic accident on the way to school than be abducted.

To the young me exploring the world with little more than a map and a ten pence piece to call for a lift home, felt like the kind of adventures I saw on TV or read about in books. The iconic explorers Scott, Shackleton and Cook, were perhaps my first inspiration, alongside Peter Duncan[3] from Blue Peter and Lee Majors[4] from The Fall Guy. A final inspiration that has run through my entire life was another TV presenter, so monumental in his field that he is famous the world over, Sir David Attenborough, whose documentaries have inspired and left me in awe of the planet on which I live.

TV was a major source of inspiration for me, and one of my first memories was of the SAS storming the Iran

---

2 Baby Dropping Ritual -

http://www.reuters.com/video/2008/04/30/indian-baby-dropping-ritual?videoId=81490

3 http://www.youtube.com/watch?v=GtQRiLDy03I

4 http://www.youtube.com/watch?v=F4LX8PPMuOY

Embassy after 26 hostages were taken by six armed terrorists. The images of the windows being blown out, followed by the black clothed, gas masked wearing soldiers abseiling in through the windows was an iconic image of the early 1980s, the 9/11 of my generation. It started a fascination in me that many schoolboys have with 'Special Forces'. As a result of witnessing the SAS in action and an episode of Duncan Dare's featuring Lofty Wiseman, I bought a copy of the SAS survival handbook. As well as telling you how to survive in a jungle or desert and what snakes not to get bitten by, there was also a method for improvising a harness and abseiling with a carpenter's G-clamp as a carabiner. Armed with this knowledge I headed to a local wood, with a piece of nylon builder's rope and the G-clamp from my toy carpentry set, and climbed 25ft up a tree. Rigging my first abseil, I readied myself for my own 'storming of the embassy'. As I kicked dramatically off the tree, the speed of my descent took me by surprise. Landing flat on my back I was convinced I had really hurt myself, and lay there motionless, winded and wondering why I was no longer attached to the rope. When I realised I was OK, I looked at that toy G-clamp, and realised it had uncurled itself. Not to be beaten I searched for and found a more substantial one, and returned for a more successful attempt.

Then my life changed. My father, who was a quantity surveyor pricing up engineering projects like the Thames Barrage for Costains, got a new job for a smaller company called Dean & Dyball in Dorset. So when I was age ten the family upped sticks and headed to Bournemouth. At first I felt alone and isolated in this booming town, but at my new school there was an outlet for the adventurous streak in me. The Local Educational Authority Maritime Training Centre was a place I went for weekly doses of water-based activities, and with it I went from being a wannabe mountaineer to a sailor.

Sailing appealed to both my adventurous spirit and my technical brain with the almost scientific discipline of analyzing the mechanics of making a dinghy perform to its limit. Applying this to racing in battered boats borrowed from the centre was an invigorating way to test both man and machine. The competitors from the local yacht club who had the advantage of a new sleek hull and fresh sails each season meant I never won, but was consistently at the front of the fleet.

This obsession ended with a friend and I sailing a small dinghy miles off the Dorset coast line, ploughing through crashing waves and somehow making it back to shore alive. That foray into the open ocean rather than the confines of the tame harbour was an amazing experience, but one my dad was rather less than impressed by. Instead of stopping me, my father got a friend to have me crew on a yacht in some races. This came to an end after I was caught one too many times in the club house of Poole Harbour Yacht Club having not signed in because I had already reached the 5 'guest visits' they allowed before I would have to join the club and the fees for even a junior members were extortionate.

When not out sailing I could often be found fishing on the banks of the river Stour or on the beach surfing on my sit on top canoe. As I prepared for my GCSEs, I faced the choice of going to the local college or the grammar school to study A-levels. That decision was taken from me by my parents' insistence that I would not learn anything at college, and they would therefore not help me financially if I went to the college. At the time I despaired at their declaration, but there was one glimmer of hope in this formal suited and booted world of that grammar school, the Combined Cadet Force. Looking back it was more like a Dad's Army for kids, as the then Commanding Officer left much of the running and organisation down to the 6th Form students. This had good and bad points. The good was we had more control over what we wanted to do, the bad being at times it would resemble the metaphorical piss up in a brewery. Testament to my dedication and focus, I could probably still strip down and clean the wonderful mechanics of an SA80 assault rifle.

The CCF was the adventurous outlet I needed. I think without it I would probably have fallen in with the wrong crowd and been another juvenile delinquent. Each half term they ran adventurous training courses all over the UK and in the space of two years I visited Scotland, The Lakes, Wales and Dartmoor on more than one occasion. On one of those first trips I met and fell into a lifelong love with rock climbing. The first time I touched rock was at the Dewerstone in Devon, a rough granite crag in a heavily wooded valley. I often wonder how I managed to climb flailing about in army surplus boots with non-stick plastic rubber soles, let alone somehow decide that this is the sport for me. The attraction was one of love at first fright and I soon purchased a new Encyclopaedia, The Handbook of Climbing by Iain Peters and Alan Fyffe. In climbing I found my passion for the outdoors, the technical analysis of equipment and a lust for adventure came together as a whole.

By the time I was seventeen, adventurous training camps were not coming round quickly enough. I had bought my own rock boots, harness and belay plate, but the rest of the equipment was too costly. There was however an alternative source, as the school had a limited selection of climbing equipment. Using the adage it is better to beg forgiveness than ask permission, each Friday afternoon when the games teachers were on the field teaching rugby Atholl and I would sneak into the office, find the key to the store, 'borrow' what we needed for the weekend adventure and reverse the whole process early on the Monday morning, before the teachers noticed.

The first place Atholl and I took our contraband was Dancing Ledge, on Dorset's Jurassic Coastline, a limestone cliff rich in fossils. At first we tentatively set up top ropes but our confidence quickly progressed beyond our actual ability and with it the idea of leading our first routes beckoned. Despite what happened next, the fascination between risk and reward has always grabbed me, the total absorption into the act of climbing lets the world pass over you, as if it is now unimportant. You are focused on something quite primal when lead climbing, walking a tightrope between life and death the decisions are real in an otherwise cartoon world.

It all went wrong for Atholl, my first climbing partner though, 25ft up Dancing Ledge. As he reached for a hold that did not exist, the expression of panic on his face was like a lost dog suddenly finding itself alone. In juxtaposition to just moments earlier when he announced to the crag that you could drop a bus on that wire it was so safe. Seconds later the expression on his face turned to one of 'Oh shit', as his right foot slipped. Scrabbling it back onto the hold, his left foot copied his right, then a hand. Time stood still for what seemed like forever as he fought to regain purchase on something, anything that would stop the inevitability of the situation. Falling like a sack of spuds, he bounced off the slab below and then smashed into the fossil encrusted limestone beach, comically followed by the wire that could reportedly hold a bus.

It seemed like a bad time to bring up the earlier argument Atholl and I had had about placing a nut into a horizontal break but, having only seen camming devices in print, what were we to do? I resisted saying 'I told you so', as Atholl looked in no shape to hear it. Whilst other climbers rushed over to his aid, I saw him start to move and, as he dusted himself off sitting up holding his broken hand, all I could do was laugh. Between my hysteria I repeatedly uttered 'It will hold a bus, hey!'.

Everyday we went climbing was a school day, albeit the school of hard knocks. In those early days climbing, the learning curve was as steep as the crags, but what I learnt about myself , the equipment and the rock has stayed with me. Before long a new bible of adventure was acquired; 'South West Climbs' by Pat Littlejohn. Armed with this and determination that still outweighed our ability it was a miracle that Atholl and I only had one accident. That ambition turned my attention to a route called *Stroof* at Subluminal on the Swanage coastline, an extreme crack climb that required the use of a Friend 1½, bought with two weeks' wages from my work as a lifeguard at the local leisure centre. That first camming device was more than a cam to me. It was to me a piece of climbing equipment from the future, a mechanical wonder that must somehow possess magical powers that make it stay in cracks. I was soon to find out that it worked when I went screaming past it having been ejected from the crux of *Stroof.* At the time I had no idea that that device linked back to Leonardo Da Vinci and Nature itself.

Approaching the end of my A-levels, I was torn between my growing passion for climbing and a more sensible choice of becoming a naval architect. The love of the outdoors had won without me knowing it. My academic grades dropped sufficiently to avoid a proper career path and, after taking a year off, I headed to Bangor University. There were many reasons for this. Paramount among them was having Snowdonia on the doorstep and secondly, it was one of the only universities that would allow someone with so few A-levels to enrol on a course.

In that year off I completed my mountain leader training at Plas Y Brenin in North Wales and needed to consolidate my skills so having the mountains so close would make that easy. Studying soon took second place to days out climbing and mountaineering. My student loan was spent not on food, accommodation or even alcohol, but on a new climbing rack, a tent and waterproofs. I somehow managed to graduate with a degree in Environmental Planning and Management but, more importantly to me, I was now qualified as a mountain leader and single pitch rock climbing instructor. In the space of three years at university, I went from a low-grade climber, to someone who was putting up new routes. I could climb moderate extremes without much concern and, more importantly, I was happy with my lot.

In my last year of University my life was about to be shaken to its core and I was already spending more and more time climbing and less studying. I spent two weeks in Norway for one attempt at the Troll Wall, Europe's biggest cliff. A few months later I was heading to Canada for ten days ice climbing when I should have been studying for my spring exams. During this period I developed a dread for early morning phone calls. My father had been taken seriously ill with a heart attack. The first call was alarming but after several repeat attacks within a year I think he knew that inevitably he would not survive. Early one morning the phone rang again, and my mum had to share the heart breaking news that my dad had died as he arrived at work that morning. School fell by the wayside, and climbing became a way I could escape the grief of losing my dad.

Somehow I managed to graduate and I settled down into a part time job at a local climbing wall with the attitude of work to live not live to work. My holidays included spending a month or more at a time in places like

Thailand, India or Yosemite. It was in the iconic valley of Yosemite where I developed a love for big wall climbing which in turn lead me to put up new routes in remote parts of Northern Canada and Alaska. It was in these places that I felt most alive, dropped off by a light aircraft in the true wilderness, days from help and totally isolated from civilisation. I finally felt like I was living my childhood dream of exploring the hardest to reach places in the world and going to places few had been to before. I was no longer following in other's footsteps but making my own in the world.

Back home in Snowdonia, I would supplement my meagre income with getting some writing and photography published in magazines. Within days of returning home from a trip to Alaska, I was shaken out of being a lost boy wandering around climbing by the sudden loss of a friend. My life suddenly seemed empty, void and without true purpose. I needed a radical shake up to get me out of the rut I had worked myself into. Within six months I had got a job as a trainee mountaineering instructor at The National Mountain Training Centre, a place that I had dreamt of working at since first attending a course over ten years ago, never believing it would happen. My boss was none other than Iain Peters, one of the authors of my first climbing book.

The knowledge I gained teaching and coaching mountain skills when working at Plas Y Brenin led to a book deal of my own and resulted in "How to Climb Harder" where I explored the science of climbing performance, and distilled it into words and pictures. Somewhere along the way to finishing that, I decided that the knowledge base for coaching in climbing was so limited that to widen it I needed to enrol on an MSc in Applied Sport Science. The head of the course, Tim Woodman, a climber and originator of much of the research in Chapter 8 that explores why we climb, asked me if I was ready to come back into academia to which I naively replied, 'yes'. Within two minutes of the first lecture I realised how unready I was. I spent the next two years studying part time and, whereas on my undergrad course, I often failed to attend my lectures, during my MSc I found myself so focused that I would occasionally sit in on other lectures and workshops for some free learning.

Beyond the knowledge that I applied to my work as a coach and a writer, there was something else that I took away from this course. That was the process of research with the need for primary sources to see the context in which knowledge was gained and its limitations. It is that context that this book helps add to the story of climbing and technology. That curiosity has lead to a constant quest to widen my knowledge and is as much a part of me as the climbing that I call my life.

The final piece of the jigsaw that shaped me was the five years I served on the Llanberis Mountain Rescue Team. In applying my mountaineering and climbing skills to effecting rescues often in difficult situations, in extreme weather and under very real time pressure. At times those rescues felt heroic and there are countless people in this world whose survival comes down to what a few extraordinary volunteers do. As well as these more dramatic rescues, there were many mundane ones where I would learn the Welsh for 'Kick up the Arse', as we held the hands of people with sprained ankles or assisted those who failed to realise that a mountain is not a walk in the park. The one part of the work I found hard to deal with was recovering inevitable fatalities. Each one hit me hard and the resulting nightmare images would haunt me for months after. I became obsessed with the causes of accidents, as behind every accident is a story of decisions and actions that often lead to disaster. It was this, mixed with social media, that eventually led to me being asked to leave the team.

All of this knowledge and experience in both living as a rock climber, and working as a mountaineering instructor are featured here in this book. Where, as well as safety aspects, part of my work also includes making days out more interesting with factoids and stories from both climbing and the natural world. This growing base of knowledge and focus of rock climbing and mountaineering, led to me finally being able to make the connections that I failed to make as a child, it is these links of knowledge that this book captures.

1 THE SPARK THAT SET THE FLAME

Every mountaineer or climber appreciates the paradox of feeling both horror and harmony when scaling wild peaks and cliffs. The shock of having to fight for survival set against an awe of Nature's beauty allows those who choose to climb and explore to experience two of the primal emotions; fear and joy. In this modern world, electronic gadgets simplify every task, risk management makes us safe and super foods make us more healthy. So is the impulse to climb a throwback to times when survival depended directly on our own actions?

Climbing as sport and pastime has only come about in the recent past. This chapter explores the possible reasons as to why that happened at all and when it occurred as it did in the 19th Century. I examine the motives of the earliest explorers to attempt to establish whether the will to conquer a mountain just happened. Or are modern climbers more closely linked to our evolutionary cousins, the climbing primates, than the veneer of civilisation would have us believe? In the course of this chapter I argue that the very same spark that set alight the flame of mountaineering had an even more startling influence on all human endeavour and our thirst for knowledge. Without that spark we might all still be walking the earth as naked apes eating nuts and berries.

Evolutionarily speaking, modern humans share a lot with primates, particularly with the chimpanzee, our closest relative. In spite of millions of years of independent evolution, it is now beyond dispute that 94% of our DNA is identical to that of the chimp. Despite lacking the anatomical equipment for spoken communication, chimps can learn sign or symbolic language and hold simple conversations. They can also beat humans in intelligence in at least the two situations described here.

Up to the age of nine months a chimp will beat a human of the same age in any intelligence test. Although humans are late starters, as soon as we make it through those nine months, we leave chimps for dust when it comes to intellect. This applies in all but one area; that of short-term memory. One research subject, a chimp called Ayumu does not just beat human opponents, he bulldozes them. He excels at a number recall test, where up to nine numbers are flashed on a computer screen in a random order and pattern for a fraction of a second. Those numbers are replaced with touchable tiles and the human or chimpanzee subject then has to remember and touch the corresponding tiles in ascending order.

Sounds easy maybe, but humans have a short-term memory that is generally limited to 7(plus or minus 2) pieces of information. What this means is that humans can process up to nine distinct pieces of information in our working memory but often this is compromised by other factors, hence the general rule of seven pieces plus or minus two. So we humans struggle to score nine on this test even with the time extended to half a second. However, when Ayumu gets going, the speed and ease with which he completes the test is mind blowing. Now we are not talking about getting those nine numbers after seeing them flash up on the screen for half a second. No, Ayumu can achieve this feat having seen the numbers flash on screen for just 60 milliseconds! That is literally in the blink of an eye. Researchers suggest that humans have lost this skill as we developed different forms of information processing such as speech and our more complex language.

We still have attributes in common with primates, a legacy from the climbing ancestors we share. These are reflexes which are supposedly present only in very young children although climbers who experience a sudden slip on a route might insist otherwise! The well-known grasp reflex is apparent from birth in human infants when their hands are brushed with an object. Immediately, fingers are clenched tightly into the palm to grasp whatever is there. This involuntary action is also present in baby primates and it enables them to hang onto their mothers' backs. In newborn children this reflex is so strong that they can support their own body weight. This fact has been tested with the aid of a washing line by at least one father I know and a quick search of 'baby pulls up' in you tube will reveal many examples of this extraordinary strength to weight[5] ratio.

We also share the Moro reflex[6] with primates. Clearly essential for the survival of the young primates travelling on the backs of their mothers, this is triggered by the feeling of becoming unbalanced or startled. A human baby reacts to the sensation by instantly reaching out its arms and pulling in and towards the chest. If you like it's an emergency reflex to grab back onto the mother if they feel themselves falling.

Another reflexive behaviour that has been observed experimentally in several infant animals is the instinctive recognition and avoidance of steep drops. The experiments[7] used what has been described as a visual cliff.

---

5 Baby performing pull ups -

http://www.youtube.com/watch?v=dXN3QFJRO-Y

6 Moro Reflex - http://www.youtube.com/watch?v=PTz-iVI2mf4

7 Original Visual Cliff Experiment - Gibson, E. J., & Walk, R. D. (1960). The "visual cliff." Scientific American, 202, 67–71.

A piece of Perspex covered the floor. Under half of it was a chequered table cloth that apparently dropped away to give the illusion of a 'cliff' although the level Perspex surface continued. In the experiment some one year old children sat on the floor side and their mothers called to them from across the 'cliff'. Out of 36 babies only 3 ventured across the cliff. As you might imagine, this is not an exclusively human response; kittens, lambs, chicks and goat kids all showed similar if not better results for cliff avoidance, some from within 24 hours of birth.

Whilst modern humans seem to be hardwired at birth with apian reflexes, we soon lose those. Our binocular vision can perceive a drop from an early age and we instinctively avoid the possibility of a fall. At first glance, the evidence suggests that underlying the human condition there is an ape in us all. However, as we develop, those inherited unconscious traits are overwhelmed by our developing consciousness.

This has been demonstrated by a re-examination of the 'visual cliff' experiment in 1985[8]. This time, the mothers were asked to show either joyful or fearful expressions. The parents who showed joy were more successful in coaxing their child over the deep end. There were considerably fewer 'jumpers' when that expression was fearful. What this suggested was that when the children reached the point where they were uncertain, they turned to their parents for confirmation. Obviously they were able to recognise and read emotions from an early age. To an extent these experiments indicate that humans may

---

[8] Re-assessing the Visual Cliff Experiments - Maternal emotional signaling: Its effect on the visual cliff behavior of 1-year-olds. James F.; Emde, Robert N.; Campos, Joseph J.; Klinnert, Mary D., Developmental Psychology, Vol 21(1), Jan 1985, 195-200.

develop risk aversion during infancy and that avoidance is influenced by parents' reactions.

Whist the evolutionary roots of the human race are revealed by its youngest members, our species is not restricted by a specialism in climbing or anything else for that matter and our success has largely come down to our versatility.

Indeed, recent medical research into injuries in young elite climbers suggests that too much specialist activity is harmful[9]. Intense training and climbing can lead to permanent finger and foot deformity. This occurs as climbers overload their digits on small holds or force feet into boots that are too tight. Finger bones which are still growing until about the age of eighteen can be damaged. Growth plates are affected causing unequal growth and the fingers become permanently twisted. But in adults frequent repetition of an activity can have a desirable outcome.

A study of elite boulderers by researchers at Bangor University[10] tested the bone mineral density of climbers' hands compared with a control group matched for age. Their findings were that these elite climbers had changed their bone structure through climbing. As a result, they had a significantly higher bone density and strength than non-climbers. This supports anecdotal evidence that a specific activity, frequently repeated, can lead to minor adaptations of the human body.

---

9 Physiological responses to rock climbing in young climbers - Audry Birute Morrison, Volker Rainer Schöffl, British Journal of Sports Medicine, 2007.

10 Athletic Profile of highly accomplished boulderers. Macdonald, J. H., Callender, N., Wilderness Environmental Medicine. 2011.

One example of such anecdotal evidence is provided by the story of St Kilda, a remote Scottish island which was inhabited for over two millennia until the small group of people who lived there were evacuated in 1930. The St Kildans were believed to have extraordinarily large toes. Whether this attribute was a genetic or a developmental adaptation has never been proved. As part of their survival strategy on the inhospitable archipelago, the St Kildans' lifestyle certainly included climbing among the biggest sea cliffs in the UK. Their meagre diet was based on subsistence farming and they caught sea birds and collected eggs from the nests on the cliffs by using ropes and a 'fowling rod'.

Unquestionably handy for sea cliff climbing, were these big toes a genetic trait or the result of so much sea bird hunting? Evolution is caused by the mutation of DNA which, after many generations, can lead to the creation of a new species. Genetic mutations occur constantly in all organisms. If a new mutation is beneficial, the individual organism is more likely to both live and mate successfully and pass on the mutated gene. The average random mutation that occurs in every generation of humans produces around 175 changes to the genetic code. That code is made up of 3.2 billion bits of information and most mutations occur in what is seen at present as 'junk code' which apparently does nothing. So it is improbable that the larger toes came about through genetics. The St Kildans' two thousand year occupation of their island was a very short time in terms of evolution. That itself limits the possibility of a beneficial genetic mutation. So I conclude that these are more likely to be adaptations caused by the activity.

Physical adaptations occur far more frequently than those caused by genetic change. This is supported by the research and anecdotal evidence as we have seen but it is actually very commonplace. When every toddler begins to walk, the bones of the legs, hips and joints must be capable of load bearing and change accordingly. So within the lifetime of every individual, bone structure alters naturally and further alterations are caused, or even brought about intentionally, by frequent repetition of a particular activity.

With this in mind, I was very interested to come across some research into whether the huge success of East African middle and long distance runners is due to their being genetically suited to the sport. The rift valley area of Kenya and the Arsi region of Ethiopia have produced a phenomenal number of world champion endurance runners. The research[11] failed to find a genetic reason and the conclusion was,

"At present it is unjustified to implicate a role for genetics in the success of East African runners when no genes have been identified as being important to their performance".

So it looks as though being brilliant at running was an effect of their way of life, nurture rather than nature then.

Fascinated as I am by theories of human evolution and the roots of our present condition and future development, I must admit that I found this surprising. But I would like to share a story about one Ethiopian runner, Haile Gebrselassie. He has won almost every long distance event and has held world records in almost as many. He started running at a young age and when he switched to competitive running he had a very strange style. One of his arms would apparently lock into his body and hardly move. He was extremely talented but his running style was very awkward. This was a learned

11 Genetic influence on East African running success, Robert A Scotta, Colin Morana, Richard H Wilson, Will H Goodwin and Yannis P Pitsiladis, Equine and Comparative Exercise Physiology, 2004

phenomenon, as he had to run over 10km to get to school and then reverse the run to get home. The locked arm was because he used to hold his books under that arm as he made the journey. Since childhood, he had been running two 10km races a day carrying a load of books. Obviously, this world class athlete's developmental history is the key factor, not his ancestry. Rather like those talented climbers, the big toed St Kildans.

Some modern humans have become extremely good at climbing. Developmental history and training causes adaptations that make them more suited to it as we have seen. I have also described some instinctive behaviours from our primate cousins which come in very handy. But we are not natural climbers. The story of Lucy confirms this.

In the history of human evolution, one of the earliest and most important fossils was that of Lucy. She was a small ape-like creature who walked the earth some 3.2 million years ago. Her bone structure showed that she and her kind had adapted from climbing to walking. That adaptation was a small difference in the shape of the base of her shin bone which indicates that Lucy could not flex her foot upwards more than 20°. Modern primates are brilliant tree climbers because the upward flexion of their feet can be as much as 40°.

In standing upright, Lucy and her descendants had freed up their hands to utilise more tools. Their thumbs became larger to oppose the forces of their fingers. This dexterity enabled them to become expert tool users and the advancement of the human race was accelerated. Armed with these tools, the speed at which humans colonised the world is staggering. Ground zero for Homo Sapiens or modern humans is a fossil found in Ethiopia that dates back two hundred thousand years. Evidence has been found of Homo Sapiens having reached Morocco, Israel and Croatia by one hundred thousand years later. The fossil record shows humans inhabiting parts of Japan, Russia and Australia by sixty thousand years after that. The latest fossil trace of early human migration was found in Chile. It was a mere ten thousand years old.

In the space of only two hundred thousand years, Homo Sapiens had managed to migrate across the globe reaching every major continent other than Antarctica. Tracing the human genome has confirmed that Homo Sapiens, our direct ancestors, did indeed migrate from Africa. They spread out across the near East and Europe, through Asia and up through what is now Russia to the Kamchatka Peninsula. They crossed the land bridge that existed only during the ice ages and most recently between fifteen thousand and six thousand years ago.

For me, the key question is what made Homo Sapiens explore and extend their territory? No scientist will be able to tell us why or how this happened. Possibly the most simple explanation is that early humans were hunter-gatherers and as their population increased, the density of their food sources decreased. They were forced to venture out into the unknown in search of food for survival. There is perhaps no stronger motivation. Remember Ayumu the super chimp? He was motivated by receiving a reward in the form of a small piece of food every time he was successful. Similarly, if you watched the linked video of a baby doing pull ups on a desk, you will notice that his motivation is the cartoon that is on the computer.

That seems very simplistic though. Perhaps I spend too much time reading about the modern explorers and mountaineers I admire. Maybe this is a romantic notion but I think, as soon as their technology enabled them to do so, surely early humans would have been as keen to explore the unknown as some of us are today.

We know from much research into both humans and other animals that positive reinforcement, or the carrot rather than the stick, is the most powerful tool for changing or strengthening behaviours. In the case of Ayumu, this motivation was supplied externally. But humans have an internal reward system. Effort and praise trigger the brain's reward centre which releases dopamine. This makes us feel good, it is pleasurable and we feel rewarded. This explains how human behaviours can be changed and how new behaviours and skills are learned. But it does not explain why some individuals are more motivated to learn and more curious than others. Undeniably, some people are driven to explore, investigate and understand the world whilst the majority are content simply to acquire enough skills to live in it.

Albert Einstein said,

"I have no special talents, I am only passionately curious".

In 2009, seven researchers from the California Institute of Technology examined human curiosity. Their work, entitled 'Curiosity as the wick that keeps the candle of learning burning'[12], provides an answer to my question about what has compelled the human race to explore the world and gather knowledge from earliest times to the present.

In outline, the experiment used an MRI scanner to measure brain activity. The students who participated were asked 40 questions designed to provoke curiosity. Examples are;

---

12 Curiosity Research -

http://authors.library.caltech.edu/22280/2/ssrn-id1308286%5B1%5D.pdf

"Which instrument was designed to sound like a human singing?"

"The Earth is part of which galaxy?"

Individually, the students were asked to rate how curious they felt about each question and how confident they were about their answers. The results showed that the questions which caused most uncertainty sparked the most curiosity. Also, curiosity peaks coincided with activity in the brain's reward centre. The students were anticipating gaining information and were hardwired to find that rewarding in itself. Interestingly, if a wrong answer had been given, the parts of the brain associated with memory and learning were activated. The experiment was repeated about two weeks later and it became clear that the students remembered best the answers to the questions that had provoked the most curiosity the first time round.

The researchers' conclusion that curiosity has a direct link to learning is elegantly summed up in the title they gave their work. They also conclude that being inquisitive is a self-motivator for discovering new things about the world because doing so triggers the brain's reward centre. Their findings surely match the childhood experiences of many of us. Personally, I failed to learn about anything that did not interest me. But if something sparked my imagination it received all my time, effort and determination to increase my knowledge. To me, the finding that **un**certainty provokes curiosity and promotes learning is fascinating. People who are always certain they are right find it hard to open their minds to new ideas. From the time of Homo Sapiens to Einstein to the present, I contend that the outstanding leaders of human advancement have always been ready to explore the unknown just because they were curious about what it would hold.

As we will see throughout this book, today we are able

answer so many questions about the world. Now our inquisitiveness is also focussed on finding answers about ourselves. Answers to uncertainties like "Can I climb that route?" or "Will I survive that Himalayan peak?" have to be found by the individual. So, by engaging in the risks associated with mountaineering, are we humans still curious to find those answers that no scientist can readily provide?

It seems likely to me that the exploration of self and the world have sparked the evolution of mountaineering and climbing as a pastime, occurring as it did on the back of the enlightenment of the world through scientific endeavour. That challenge and desire for knowledge was also an essential part of our development and success as humans. As we have seen, curiosity was the spark that set the flame of technology and science.

Early technologies that were essential for ancient peoples to put down roots were fire, stone tools, metals, the wheel and the plough. It is within these first civilisations that humans started to engage with the mountains. The earliest civilised people seem to have held elevated places in high esteem. This might be because those cultures were striving to understand the sun's annual migration in the sky. Many primitive structures were built to follow celestial movements. These included burial mounds and various Henges to track the passing of the seasons. Later these buildings took on religious significance and started reaching for the sky. Was this an effort to get closer to the heavenly bodies which dictated peoples' lives?

The oldest example of a religious building, the Gobeki Tepe is situated on a mountain ridge in South East Turkey. There is also evidence that many early civilisations used caves and cliffs for safety and security from aggressive neighbours, including the Dogons of Mali[13] and the Anasazi in America. This reverence of high places is also reflected in many early structures. The Pyramids of Egypt, the stepped towers of the Incan and Mayan people and the Greek Parthenon are all either miniature mountains or situated on raised areas. These associations though give us no real evidence of mountaineering as a recreational activity.

One of the results of civilisation was written language which helped us trace climbing back through historic records. The earliest reference to rock climbing is a Chinese watercolour from 400BC depicting men climbing rocks. However, climbing may have dated back further than that as an early Chinese Empire used the 1500m peak, Thai Shan, as a place of religious pilgrimage for over 3000 years. The Silk Route was an ancient means to cross the Himalaya. It linked the Chinese with the Indus River civilisations and on into the Near East and Europe. It was being used for trade by around 200BC but there is evidence of its use from around 1600BC. This early Himalayan crossing was enormously important but it was simply a means to trade between East and West.

The earliest evidence of people exploring and interacting with the mountains for reasons other than trade or religion only came to light in September 1991. Two tourists stumbled across a body partially frozen into a glacier three thousand metres up the Finailspitze on the Austrian/Italian border. Thinking it to be a modern mountaineer, the local police recovered the body and it was sent to the University of Innsbruck. Immediately identified as pre-historic, Ötzi the iceman, as he has since become known, lived 5300 years ago. His story is a

---

13 http://www.youtube.com/watch?v=N70DLM8Az_8 - Catherine Destivelle soloing up the Dogon cliffs.

fascinating one. Never before had such well preserved early human remains been found.

The content of his stomach showed that he ate a meal of Chamois meat and grain 8 hours before his death. Study of his bones showed he often walked long distances over hilly terrain, adding support to the idea that he was perhaps a high-altitude shepherd. How he came to die on the side of that mountain was first put down to being caught out in a winter storm but the pollen evidence in his stomach suggested he died in the spring. Ten years after his discovery, his body was moved from Austria to Italy after the Italians claimed he was discovered on their side of the border. He received another CT scan which revealed that he was in fact shot in the back by an arrow and was perhaps running for his life. Other DNA evidence suggests that he did not go quietly. He had shot and retrieved an arrow from at least two victims. He also had numerous injuries to his hands and face and his burial position suggested that someone had rolled him onto his front to remove the arrow which killed him.

Whilst just his presence in the mountains is of interest to mountaineers, his equipment is even more intriguing. He had a quiver of arrows in various states of completion, a flint knife, a copper axe and a longbow. On his feet were well made shoes of leather which were possibly even designed to cross snow as they were waterproof and wide. However a British scientist, Jacqui Wood, has gone one stage further than that. She suggests that these boots were the upper part of a fairly elaborate 'snowshoe', the wooden frame of which had previously been mistaken for a backpack. His snowshoes would be the first piece of technology designed specifically for mountain travel ever discovered.

These early interactions with the mountains will have

inevitably led to many summits being climbed. It took until 663AD for the first recorded ascent to be made when an unnamed monk climbed Mount Fuji. This was more an act of worship as the mountain was a sacred place. Now, some 1500 years later, it is still a pilgrimage for many who climb the peak overnight in order to watch the rising sun which famously features on the Japanese flag.

Across in South America, mountains were used for an altogether more gruesome religious purpose. Like the stepped temples, they were used for human sacrifice. This was discovered when three bodies were found on the summit of Llullaillaco, a 6739m high volcano on the Chilean/Argentine border. This story is all the more horrifying because these were the bodies of children left mummified on the peak. Modern forensic scientists have established from hair, bone and tissue samples that they were drugged for up to three months on maze beer and coca before they were marched to the summit and left to perish, some five hundred years ago.

The first recorded ascent of a mountain simply for the sake of the achievement itself was in Europe. King Charles VIII of France ordered that Mont Aiguille be climbed in 1492. This perhaps best illustrates the King's curiosity as there was no reason for the ascent other than to fulfil the whim of their monarch. This isolated peak in the Vercors Plateau of the Prealps is just outside Grenoble. The peak is surrounded on all sides by steep cliffs and looks inaccessible so there is no doubt that it was first climbed just to see if it could be done. Antoine De Ville, one of the King's servants, set out and made an ascent via an elaborate combination of artificial aids and ladders thereby making the World's first Via Ferrata.

It was however the ascent of Mount Blanc that was the

first major milestone in mountaineering. In 1786, Jacques Balmat and Michael Paccard made the first ascent of the White Mountain. This was a massive breakthrough with the route dominated by snow, ice, glaciers and crevasses. The pair used alpen stocks and axes to make their ascent and these were among the first tools adapted specifically for the pastime of mountaineering. The attempt was instigated by Horace-Benedict de Saussere who offered a reward for the first team to reach the summit. Horace, who had attempted the mountain the year before via the Dome du Gouter route, was no doubt trying to satisfy his curiosity as to whether the peak could successfully be scaled. Balmat and Paccard made their ascent through the much more complex Grand Mulets' route. Whilst technically an easier climb, the fields of seracs and crevasses made the objective danger higher. On August 8th of that year they succeeded and alpinism started to blossom.

The alpen stock was the alpine tool of choice at the time. It was a long wooden spear with an iron tip. It was a very rudimentary tool for glacier travel, described by one early mountaineering writer as being more for 'moral' support than a physical one. It was often used in conjunction with a hand axe that closely resembled those we still use for cutting wood. The two were later merged into the ice axe we know today.[14]

The ascent of Mont Blanc was the starting gun for mountaineering as a pastime and ultimately a sport. On the back of this ascent the 'men of leisure', the tycoons of their generation with vast supplies of money and ample time to enjoy themselves, started to turn to the mountains

---

14 There is a brief history of the development of the ice axe at the BMC website, we shall revisit this history later though:
http://thebmc.co.uk/Feature.aspx?id=1791

in search of adventure but also something more ephemeral. The 18th Century saw the explosion of the Romantic Movement. This was an artistic, literary and intellectual movement. It was partly aimed at trying to redefine the aristocracy and social norms of the times but it was also a reaction to the coming of the age of scientific endeavour. In trying to put aesthetic experience to the fore, the romantic poets, writers and artists were redefining the emotional response to the feelings of trepidation, fear and awe evoked by facing nature head on.

Romanticism has been described as the springboard for the outdoor revolution that it undoubtedly inspired. But was this movement just an extension and expression of human curiosity? The enlightenment of Science had started answering fundamental questions about the world. In response, did people   search out the kind of experiences that science simply could not address? I think they did because this period saw many great explorers setting out to attempt to reach the diminishing number of places left on which humans had yet to stand.

Indeed Shackleton's infamous invite to his epic voyage to Antarctica at the beginning of the 20th century read, *"Men wanted for hazardous journey. Low wages, bitter cold, long hours of complete darkness. Safe return doubtful. Honour and recognition in event of success."* [15]. Would anyone have signed up for such an absurd request, had the tradition of adventure and wonder of the world not been promoted by the Romantics?

The essence of much of the Romantic sentiment has been embraced by climbers through their endeavours in mountaineering right up to the present day. I am convinced that the affect of Romanticism on

---

15 The Times circa 1912 (This is possibly refutable)

mountaineering has been powerful and its influence should not be overlooked. That affect on the ethos of climbing runs so deep that one of the first scientific investigations in to the motivations behind participation in high risk expeditions proposed that some form of 'spiritual enlightenment' would occur. The researcher based this on his study of mountaineering literature where numerous stories of these ephemeral moments are recalled[16].

While Romanticism was partly a response to the growing enlightenment brought about by what the Romantics saw as cold, hard science, undeniably it was the scientists who led the push to better understand the world. Newton was the foremost of course, inspired to derive his gravitational theory by a falling apple. It has been asserted that the apple incident never happened but William Stukeley gave this account of a meeting with Newton;

"…*We went into the garden, & drank tea under the shade of some apple trees, only he, & myself. Amidst other discourse, he told me, he was just in the same situation, as when formerly, the notion of gravitation came into his mind. 'why should that apple always descend perpendicularly to the ground,' thought he to him self: occasion'd by the fall of an apple, as he sat in a contemplative mood: 'why should it not go sideways, or upwards? but constantly to the earth's centre?*

To support his universal theory of gravitation, Newton proposed a series of experiments. He devised one which would determine the mass of the Earth but he believed it would be too difficult to measure and abandoned the effort. The experiment, when it was eventually carried out by someone else, became more widely known as the

---

16 We explore these ideas in Chapter 7 when we explore the age old question of 'Why We Climb', and try to eradicate the notion that there is more to this argument than '….because its there'.

'Schiehallion Experiment'. Not only did it broaden the understanding of gravity but it also had a direct influence on mapping the mountains. As a result of the experiment 'contour lines' were first used on land-based maps.

Contour lines did not appear on the earliest maps which to us look ludicrously simple. Often these had little resemblance to the actual land depicted because they were usually drawn from a distance at sea. But the purpose of the earliest maps was not navigation. They were often used as political leverage in land disputes where he with the best map won the territory. As a mountaineer and instructor, I find it fascinating how we came to have this particularly handy little addition to our maps. Contours show a great deal of detail and can help anyone navigating through mountains to avoid cliffs and unnecessary trudging uphill by revealing the shape of the land. They are perhaps one of the most under used aids but to me they are the backbone of any mapping system.

The story of the humble contour line is an interesting one which begins with the   experiment designed by Newton; the first reasonably accurate attempt to discern the mass of the earth. His plan was to find a conical shaped mountain standing in isolation and to use two pendulums, one on either side of it. His theory of gravity predicted that the mountain would have a small gravitational affect on the pendulums, pulling them towards the centre of the mountain. As the pendulums were on opposite sides of the mountain, the difference between the angle of each pendulum and the vertical could be ascertained. Newton believed that the deflection would be too small to measure so into the story come some scientists who were prepared to go to find the right mountain.

A pair of French astronomers first attempted the experiment in 1738 on a mountain in Ecuador. This intrepid pair did conclude that the Earth was not an empty shell but they were so hampered by the wildness of the conditions that they could not complete the experiment. So in 1773, the Royal Society decided to send out the astronomer and surveyor Charles Mason to find a suitable mountain in the UK. He returned from Scotland with the name Schiehallion, an isolated peak on Rannoch Moor just outside Fort William. Mason turned down the job of carrying out the experiment, leaving it to Nevil Maskelyne, Charles Hutton and Reuben Burrow. However, a few historians suggest that Maskelyne was never very hands on and that he left the measurements and the mathematics to Hutton and Rueben.

How did this experiment then lead to the use of contour lines on land-based maps? Sea floor contour lines had been in use for some years due to the importance placed on keeping the great naval fleets and trade vessels from running aground. The use of land-based contours was virtually unheard of but they were going to be needed in this experiment because one of the measurements required was the volume of the mountain. Combining the volume of the mountain with the density of the rock from which it was formed would give a close approximation of the mountain's mass.

Hutton surveyed the mountain and produced thousands of spot heights a known distance apart. To use these measurements to calculate a volume was tricky. He decided to interpolate points of equal height between these surveyed points and by joining them together, he created a series of concentric rings and the contour line on a land based map had been invented. The mathematics for working out the volume of a truncated cone already existed and the contour lines essentially defined a stack of truncated cones. The volume of the whole mountain could now be found, the density of the rock was known and a relatively simple calculation determined the mass of Schiehallion.

Knowing the mass of Schiehallion the team now dangled the two pendulums either side of it. Without the mountain, the pendulums would have hung vertically in a direct line with the centre of the Earth. But the mountain's pull caused a deflection from the vertical which was found by taking a transit sighting along the pendulums to points in the night sky and measuring the difference. Knowing the weight of the pendulum and the amount of the deflection they could now measure the force of the mountains attraction and with it they could now derive the mass of our planet.

Newton, like Albert Einstein, was blessed with a passionate curiosity which brought about his great discoveries. Curiosity has compelled scientists to answer many questions about the world and in this chapter I have argued that curiosity is the invisible but essential guide that has led humans along a path that started with a single step made by an ape and continues to lead us into the future.

We started this chapter by exploring our evolutionary roots for answers as to why we climb. Whilst there are many things we share with our closest relatives, clearly there are also things that set us apart. One of those defining parts of being human then is our natural inquisitiveness and how that enquiry into the world provides intrinsic motivation. This self-perpetuating need for discovery and knowledge led humans out of Africa and on to form civilisation.

Why those early societies held high places in such esteem is something of a mystery. Across the globe towering structures or mountainous settings were very much a part of society even when they were places of sacrifice. It was within those early civilisations the first written language developed and with it the ability to store and pass on knowledge. That accumulating intelligence led us along a path which included Newton arriving at the mass of the earth. It was the Age of Reason that provoked the backlash of the Romanticists who, in trying to explore the emotions, self and nature, started to explore the World's wilder places.

What these early exploits in mountaineering, technology and science reflect though is not so much a passion for the mountains for their own sake, *labor ipse voluptas*[17], but one of trying to conquer the unknown and satisfy our curiosity about these hidden worlds for the sake of knowledge be that worldly or heavenly. The year 1849[18] was the last year in which there was no ascent of Mont Blanc. Less than a century after the first ascent it was starting to become something of a trade route and Mountaineering as a pastime was being born. I believe that was due to the intrinsic reward we gain from satisfying our curiosity by meeting the challenge of exploring the unknown. But that is only part of the story. The other reasons why modern humans engage in risk-based activities are for a later chapter.

---

17 Roughly translates to 'Labour itself is Pleasure'.

18 This comes from Volume 16 of The Badminton Library of Sports and Pastimes that can be viewed online at.

http://badminton.exato.nl/books/library/mountaineering/

2 THE EARLY PIONEERS AND THE GOLDEN AGE OF EXPLORATION

I was once asked on the social media phenomenon that is twitter to describe exploration. For those of you who are unaware, tweeting is best described as life in 140 characters or less. I came up with the succinct definition, "*Explorers go where no one has gone before the rest of us merely follow in their footsteps*". I was thinking of mainly exploration into the wild and remote places on Earth but to a certain extent it applies to all aspects of humanity. Those at the forefront of any endeavour, be it sporting or scientific, are stepping into the unknown and touching the extreme boundaries of the world and in doing so they come to know something of its true splendour[19]. There are many people throughout human history who have possessed the required mix of intellect, curiosity and bravery to push at the perceived limits of our world. In attempting to widen the knowledge of humankind, pioneering mountaineers and scientists

---

19 In the last part of that sentence I paraphrase part of Maurice Herzog's introduction to 'Annapurna'. He wrote of surviving an epic ascent, when convalescing in a hospital bed;

> "*In overstepping our limitation, in touching the extreme boundaries of man's world, we have come to know something of its true splendor. In my worse moments of anguish, I seemed to discover the deep significance of existence of which till then I had been unaware. I saw it was better to be true than to be strong. The marks of the ordeal are apparent on my body. I was saved and I have won my freedom. This freedom, which I shall never lose, has given me the assurance and serenity of a man who has fulfilled himself. It has given me a rare joy of loving that which I used to despise. A new splendid life has opened out before me.*"

alike had to approach the unknown with very little collective experience to guide them. By fathoming the great uncertainties, they found out the hard way so much that we now take for granted.

The period covered in this chapter spans the early forays into the alpine regions prior to 20th Century to the outbreak of the First World War, often described as the Golden Age of Mountaineering. It was a period when mountaineers were "Killing Dragons"[20]. Folklore and mythical stories were often used to describe the inaccessible regions of snow and ice that hitherto were beyond men's desire. Enlightenment had started to change the understanding of the world and climbers were no longer kept at bay by mythology. Instead, a new romantic movement promoted interaction with Nature to experience the shock and awe of facing the wilderness head on. As a result, the mountaineers of the age seemed hell bent on showing they were superior to nature and could place a human anywhere on the planet.

Many of the leading mountaineers of the day experienced the double edged sword of the risk and reward of mountaineering. Some mountaineers were obsessed with making hard and difficult ascents on the lesser peaks of the world whilst others turned to the higher but technically easier peaks of Himalaya. Whatever the objective, a few of the early pioneers often paid the

---

20 Killing Dragons: The Conquest of the Alps by Fergus Flemming covers this period thoroughly. The idea that dragons occupied the high Alps has several origins. Reportedly, Peter III of Aragon claimed in jest to have seen a dragon whilst on an ascent of a peak in the Pyrenees. This was followed by a naturalist Wagner who wrote of Dragons in 1680 and claimed to know a man, John Tinner, who not only saw but shot one twelve years before. It was a full seven feet long, of a blackish grey, its head like a cat's and it had no feet.

ultimate price for their exploration. Wilfred Owen, one of the Great War poets, wrote '*Ducle et decorum est pro parti mori*'; 'Sweet and right is to die for one's country'. In this era alpinists seemed to live by the motto that it was also sweet and right to die for a belief in what could be achieved. The do or die attitude to exploration is epitomised by Laurence Oates' immortal words "*I am going outside, I may be sometime*" as he sacrificed himself and saved his fellow explorers from witnessing a slower and more tortuous end. It was though the tactics employed by Scott, his leader on the British Antarctic Expedition, that led to the deaths of the whole team. At first Scott was seen as a tragic hero but now in the light of a better understanding we know that early decisions he made about everything from the diet to the equipment doomed the expedition from its outset, making it something of a fool's errand. This is highlighted by Amundsen's efficiency. He not only beat Scott to the Pole, although he arrived in the Antarctic a couple of months after him, he also returned alive having successfully reached the South Pole before Scott and his final team perished on the ice cap.

If early exploration was so fraught with danger what motivated these early explorers? Was it the individual's dream or political influence? Or can we return to the idea of curiosity laid out in the previous chapter as a driving force? To be honest there are probably many reasons why people chose to climb. What we can be sure about is that conquering alpine peaks and reaching the Poles were at times a statement of imperial ambition and a quest for world dominance. Yet somehow mountaineering still seems to have remained a personal battle for fulfilment by the individuals who boldly went where no man had gone before. These early explorers were balancing on a tightrope between celebrity and infamy.

In Europe these golden days of Alpinism were typified

by first ascents of the plentiful supply of unclimbed peaks of every conceivable shape, size and difficulty. Amongst all those peaks was one grand prize, a mountain so iconic that merely writing down its name puts an image of a near perfect pyramidal peak into the mind. This towering canine tooth of rock and ice was for years

seen as impossible. The Matterhorn was the scene of many epics as mountaineers lined up to attempt to stand upon its summit. It would eventually fall to a wood engraver from London whose other job as an illustrator for a publishing company led him to visit the Alps on an assignment. Vowing to become a mountaineer, Edward Whymper went onto fulfil that dream. His most quoted phrase is,

"Climb if you will, but remember that courage and strength are naught without prudence, and that a momentary negligence may destroy the happiness of a lifetime[21]*"*.

Whymper is synonymous with the history of the Matterhorn as he not only made the first ascent, but arguably penned that phrase as a direct result of what occurred on that fateful July day in 1865. That quote is etched into my subconscious as nearly every day for a year I passed a plaque on which it was engraved. It served as a constant reminder that in the vertical world of mountaineering getting to the top is only half way or, as some mountaineers put it, getting to the top is optional, getting back down is mandatory.

The Ascent of the Matterhorn was more than just an ascent by gentlemen and their mountain guides. Two teams approached the mountain almost simultaneously from either side; an Anglo-Swiss team attempting the Hornli ridge from Switzerland and an Italian team coming

---

21 There is some evidence to suggest that this quote came from his guide on the Matterhorn, and not Whymper himself, although it is generally credited to Whymper.

up the Italian ridge. Each team was aware of the other's summit bid, but there was no rush on the ascent, the mountain had already seen off several attempts.

Whymper's team was large and was only fully formed the evening before when his group met another over dinner in the Monte Rosa Hotel in Zermatt and realised they had a common objective, the Matterhorn. Whymper had planned to climb with Lord Francis Douglas and had arranged to be guided by the two Peter Taugwalders, a Swiss father and son team. In the hotel prior to their departure, they met Charles Hudson and his inexperienced friend Douglas Hadow who had employed the famous French guide Michael Croz. The two groups decided to team up for the ascent.

The following day the seven men made steady progress up the Hornli ridge. The mountain had thwarted all previous attempts and even when Whymper's team reached the long summit ridge they were still unsure if they had been beaten by the Italians or not. Looking down the other side they saw the Italians below. According to his own account, it was at this point that Whymper reflected that the sheer commitment to the Matterhorn by the leader of the Italian party entitled him more than anyone to be first to stand on the summit. This humility did not extend to the emotional high of success though when Whymper, victorious, shouted down at the Italians from the top before trundling rocks towards them for emphasis!

Having made the summit, Whymper's team turned round and started the descent that would prove the group's undoing. Hadow, the most inexperienced member of the team, was being guided step by step down the mountain by Croz. Losing his footing, Hadow knocked Croz off balance and, like dominoes linked by a single strand of hemp rope, one followed another followed another. All members of the team should have fallen to their deaths and the story of the ascent would have been lost or retold by the Italians. Luck though was on Whymper's side. He and his guides braced themselves for the inevitable plummet down the sheer face. The rope suddenly went taut and then snapped. Frozen to the spot, they watched as Hadow, Croz, Hudson and Douglas fell 4000ft. The body of Douglas was never found, all of the others are buried in the graveyard in Zermatt.

This was quite typical of the type of accident in the Alps and elsewhere for that matter. Being roped up with no protection between team members can add as much risk as it takes away. A quick study of the recent editions of the American Alpine Club's annual report on accidents in North America will often show numerous accidents with four telltale letters after them; RUNP indicating 'Roped Up No Pro'. Despite numerous technological advancements over the years this type of accident is still a prevalent killer in alpine travel.

A similarly gruesome accident happened in 2002 on Mt Hood[22]. In a repeat of the circumstances of the Whymper incident on the Matterhorn, one climber lost his footing and started to fall. However that climber was the top person in a four man roped team and, as he accelerated down the mountain, the other three climbers dropped into a position to arrest the fall but were unable to stop him. One by one, as the rope went tight, they were ripped off the side of the mountain. So now there were four people careering downwards, straight towards another pair of climbers roped together. Both are cheese wired off their feet and follow the now growing number of climbers,

---

22 Here's a report from the Mt Hood incident:

http://www.traditionalmountaineering.org/Report_Hood_Bergschrund.htm

ropes, crampons and ice axes as they speed down the mountain. The third group of three climbers below them stood even less of a chance than the others and they too joined the rest accelerating toward the bergschrund at the base of the face. In all, nine climbers came to rather abrupt stop in the crevasse. Three died, four had major injuries, one had minor injuries and somehow one of them survived relatively unscathed.

Moving simultaneously whilst roped together on easy snow and ice saves time. However, accidents like these means it can arguably be safer not to be roped up at all or, better still, actually pitch sections where the consequences of a slip are high. This was highlighted by a few accidents involving mountain guides around the world where both client and guide have come to grief. This sparked research into just how much force a trained mountain guide can arrest when holding a rope. It showed that, unless the fall is stopped almost immediately, the chances of stopping an adult sliding on moderately steep, hard neve ice are practically zero.

In the Whymper case, the attempt to stop the first three who fell failed because the hemp rope was woefully weak. In snapping, it probably saved Whymper and his guides. Although state of art for the time, the rope had no real stretch to absorb the impact so the shock load was very high. As a result, if someone did fall and that fall was stopped without snapping the rope, then the energy involved was high enough to break a climber's back. For these reasons the early pioneers' maxim 'The leader never falls' was not idle advice, the lives of everyone on the team would have depended on it.

Historically this was a very interesting time. Until five years before Whymper's ascent, the vast majority of the world believed in some form of divine creation. In 1859

Darwin started to change all that with his radical new ideas of the process of evolution through natural selection. In doing so, he set in motion a gradual change in belief that is still going on today. Similarly, many of the home comforts such as electricity which we now take for granted were being developed for the mass market for the first time. Whilst electricity had been understood for some time, a practical application had not yet been found[23]. Engineers were starting to make their mark on the earth, with the Suez canal being completed by 1869 and, at around the same time in America, the first trans-continental railroad was completed. In 1867, Alfred Nobel formulated a new substance called dynamite which had immense potential for good but it would also be used as a weapon of such devastating power that it would redefine warfare. After Nobel's brother died, a French paper ran Alfred's obituary by mistake condemning the death and destruction that his inventions had caused. Struck by this awful legacy, in 1897 Nobel set about leaving a much more noble bequest when he signed a will leaving the majority of his fortune to found the Nobel Prizes. These are awarded for eminence

---

23 Obviously Electricity has been around us ever since the start of civilization, and even before that, and to a certain extent we did have an understanding of it at the time. Benjamin Franklin, he of the $100 bill, flew his famous kite into a storm way back in 1752 to prove lightning was electricity. By the early 1800s, Faraday had discovered that electricity could be generated by passing a magnetic field through a wire coil. Finally, Thomas Edison gave us a use for electricity when he literally had a light bulb moment. My favourite quote attributed to Edison is "Genius is 1% inspiration and 99% perspiration", sweat on. Interestingly, there were at least twenty-two people prior to Edison who developed types of light bulb. However it was Edison's use of a better filament that was more incandescent and had a higher resistance as well as managing to achieve a higher vacuum that resulted in his being the first viable version.

in Physical Science, Chemistry, Medical Science, Literature and the last   is general and has become known as the 'Nobel Peace Prize'.

The scientific knowledge gained during the period of enlightenment was beginning to be used for practical purposes, which led to the industrialisation of the world through the division of labour and the development of mega cities. The technological advances that started in these new industries became mainstream and were eventually used in mountaineering. That development of new technology started to occur in this period as equipment was refined specifically for use by climbers.

Paccard and Balmat had just an alpen stock and essentially a wood axe on their ground breaking ascent of Mount Blanc in 1786. But in 1865 Whymper had a mountaineering ice axe, one of the first items of equipment specifically designed for climbing. Its invention is credited to Grivel around 1840. The company is still a leading manufacturer of ice climbing equipment today. Their original blacksmith workshop was situated in Les Forges in Argentiere where many mountaineers passed and called in to exchange ideas. However Grivel do not consider themselves to have invented the axe. What they did was listen to the opinions and ideas of climbers and alter the design. Mr Alfred Wills, perhaps the first chronicler of the ice-axe, confirms that they tweaked a design which already existed. He suggests in his book on the high Alps that the design in fact came from the Oberland guides he took with him on Mont Blanc.

' The sticks the Oberland men carried were admirably suited for their work. They were stout pieces of undressed wood, with the bark and knots still upon them, about four feet long, shod with a strong iron point at one end, and fixed at the other into a heavy iron head, about four inches long each way; one arm being a sharp spike, with

which to hew out the ice, where needed, the other wrought into a flat blade with a broad point, something like a glazier's knife. . . This kind of alpenstock is hardly ever seen at Chamouni . . . the great utility of the Oberland implement called forth repeated expressions of admiration from the Chamouni men, to whom it was new.' - Wanderings in the High Alps, A. Wills (1858)

What Grivel did was to take this prototype from the Oberland and make it their own by refining the design, a simple enough idea but one that had to wait for a chance encounter. In combining the designs they made such a classic tool that a mountaineering ice axe today is virtually identical to Grivel's first ice axe although now the shaft is made from aluminium instead of wood. The new design allowed steps to be cut more easily in frozen snow and ice. Some references to this technique go back as far as the 1820s. It was possibly employed prior to this by chamois hunters and maybe even by Ötzi as he fled from his pursuers across the glacier which preserved his body.

Whilst Whymper had ice axes, the modern form of the crampon had to wait until the next century when, in 1908, Oscar Eckenstein 'invented' the 10-point crampon; ten metal spikes on a frame which is strapped to the boot for traction on snow and ice. Earlier 'climbing-irons' are described in various texts, in particular a version which fitted around the heel. Early references have described these as having '6, 8 or more spikes'. Maybe Eckenstein was wrongly credited with the original concept but his refinements produced crampons that closely resemble those we see today. He also pioneered the idea of shortening the ice axe, then over a metre long. This trend has continued to recent times and now an ice axe for mountaineering is usually around 70cm in length. The tweaking of classic designs has a long history in both climbing and technology in general. In climbing equipment, the development has been focused on improving safety, ease of use and greater specialization for mountaineering.

The early climbers did not have crampons though. Instead they had boots with a series of specially shaped nails driven into the sole. By 1892 the Badminton Library already had advice on how to best attach the nails to the boot. This suggested turning over the top of the nail after driving it into the sole or drilling a small hole and wetting it before hammering the nail in. The rusting of the nail then helped to secure it in place.

A second consideration for nails was the material they were made from with a preference for wrought rather than cast iron. Scientifically this makes lots of sense. Wrought iron is both tough and malleable due in part to having less than 1 % carbon and being worked by the blacksmith's hammer helps align the iron molecules and reduce the carbon content. Cast iron has much more carbon, between 3% and 4.5%. Although it is tougher than wrought iron, it is more brittle and this would be exacerbated by low temperatures when mountaineering boots were worn in snow and ice.

There was also another material that could have been used but at the time its cost was prohibitive. Its use has been traced back through archaeology to 4000 years ago. The material is steel which is essentially iron that, through the process of forging, has literally had the crap or carbon beaten out of it. It required lots of working on the anvil and repeated heating in the furnace so it could take weeks to make a single item which would therefore be very expensive. In 1855, a more efficient process for manufacturing steel was promised by British metallurgist Sir Henry Bessemer.

He noticed that iron ore left above the smelting fire would turn to steel on the external surfaces where the effect of contact with the air was to burn off carbon. In 1856, he refined the process with the invention of his 'converter' to make steel easier and cheaper to manufacture. However, his early attempts proved rather unsuccessful and he was on the brink of failure. His problem was that, without knowing the exact carbon content of the ore being smelted, it was near impossible to gauge how much carbon to remove by pumping air through the molten iron. Another metallurgist, Robert Forester Mushet, came up with a simple and elegant solution which is used to this day. He proposed removing all the carbon from the iron before adding the exact amount of carbon back into to the molten iron resulting in steel.

This idea turned Bessemer's fortunes around and he fought to protect his patents including secretly financing *Engineering*, a newspaper that unsurprisingly backed his patent claims. In 1866, Robert Mushet's 16-year-old daughter made a journey to Bessemer's offices in London and confronted him with the fact that his success was based on her father's work. We will never know if Bessemer's patent on this issue would have stood up in court because he elected instead to pay Mushet the considerable sum of £300 a year, a payment that he continued to make for 25 years.

Steel was seen as a wonder material then. It was tougher than wrought iron but without the brittleness of cast iron. The technological applications seemed endless. Steel held a sharp edge better than iron, was stronger under tension and more resistant to shock. In the world of an expanding railway network, readily available steel meant that tracks no longer needed to be replaced as often as every 8 weeks. It promised an end to a series of horrific accidents caused by collapsing bridges. Built from cast and wrought iron which are strong under compression but weakened by tension and bending, at least four bridges collapsed between 1847 and 1879. The most infamous of these happened on a stormy night in December 1879 when a train was crossing the Tay estuary. Strong winds were blamed for putting sideways stresses on the bridge which failed catastrophically as the locomotive passed over it. The train with all 6 carriages plunged into the stormy estuary where 75 people lost their lives. Steel was opening up a brighter, safer future for all but most importantly for climbers, it offered the possibility of a better ice axe.

Whilst engineers like Isambard Kingdom Brunel, Thomas Telford, George Stephenson, the Roebling's in America, Bessemer and Mushet were changing the world in the 1800s, one man is credited with changing the game of mountaineering by inventing 'modern alpinism'. Albert Fredrick Mummery made numerous first ascents in the Alps and beyond but it was his novel approach that changed how mountaineers approached the blossoming sport. Mummery was short sighted and had a physical deformity but in spite of this he excelled in the mountains. He also invented the Mummery Tent made from oiled silk that weighed less than two pounds. Like Whymper though, Mummery was all too aware of the fragility of life in such places. This is reflected in his, *My Climbs in the Alps and Caucasus* published in 1894, in which the final chapter was entitled 'The Pleasure and Penalties of Mountaineering'.

Previously, vast hoards of equipment were often used to besiege the mountains and conquer their summits. Mummery instead went with a fast and light approach. Rather than a deliberate act to revolutionise alpinism, some people now believe that his motives were less grand and more personal. Firstly, his physical deformity prevented him from carrying heavy loads and forced him to go fast and light. Secondly, his eyesight was so poor that his route finding was atrocious as Norman Collie once wrote on him,

'Mummery was not good in knowing what was the best way up a mountain'.

This led to him having to climb out of some situations that turned out to be groundbreaking territory. More than this though, Mummery was also one of the first mountaineers to start to shun the idea of using Mountain Guides. Instead he developed his own self-supported approach. Having made the first ascent of the Zmutt Ridge on the Matterhorn with guides, he later returned to climb it self-supported with a friend.

Mummery was scaling the highest peaks not only in the Alps but he also ventured into the Himalayas. Then no one, including Mummery, was aware of the exact effects of extreme altitude when exploring that harsh environment. Climbers were chronicling the headaches, fatigue and other symptoms of 'mountain sickness' but at that time it was put down to stagnant or bad air. It is almost certain that mountaineers were experiencing Acute Mountain Sickness and possibly High Altitude Pulmonary Oedema and Cerebral Oedema. Whilst there is little evidence to suggest that many climbers died directly from the effects of extreme altitude, these may well have been contributing factors to many early alpine accidents. It is, after all, the risks we are unaware of that are most likely to kill us.

The ignorance of those Himalayan pioneers reminds me of one of the most widely known scientists who carried out groundbreaking work at the end of the 19th century and into the next. Like Mummery, Marie Curie changed the game when it came to both physics and chemistry; so much so that she is the only person to have won Nobel Prizes in two different fields of research. She discovered two elements Polonium and Radium, studied radiation with her husband and did pioneering work in oncology. But like the mountaineers who were unaware of the affects of altitude on their bodies, Marie Curie was facing a hidden ticking time bomb as she experimented with some of the most radioactive substances, totally unprotected from their effects. She was discovering ways that cancers could be treated with radioactivity but was at the same time slowly poisoning herself. In 1934, she died of aplastic anaemia brought about by prolonged exposure to radiation. She and her husband undoubtedly pushed at the boundaries of our world and, by defining and researching radiation, helped pave the way that has led to further great discoveries. But their naivety with radioactive materials cost her her health and ultimately her life.

Mummery's writing on the risk and reward of climbing can be equally applied to the Curies. Their story highlights that we never set out to die. Instead, the taking of risks, whether consciously or not, allows us to reap rewards that have to be experienced and understood to be expressed in words. His insight into mountaineering in the 19th century is still valid today and one of the more light hearted quotes from *My Climbs in the Alps and Caucasus* is,

"It has frequently been noticed that all mountains appear doomed to pass through the three stages: An inaccessible peak - The most difficult ascent in the Alps - An easy day for a lady."[24]

In 1895, the year after that book was published, Mummery headed to the Himalayas attempting to make one of his trademark lightweight alpine style attempts on Nanga Parbat. His chapter on the risks that mountaineers

---

24 This slightly sexist statement perhaps reflects the times, although Mummery often climbed with either his wife or her friend Lily Bristow. It is also apparent that from an early age women engaged in mountaineering, as there is advice in the 1892 Badminton Library publication on Mountaineering for the 'Climbing Outfits for Ladies'.

take stands all the more true after he and two Gurkha Sherpas were swept to their death by an avalanche on the mountain.

As the dawn of the twentieth century broke, mountaineering continued to evolve and more specialist equipment was developed. Possibly one of the most common pieces of climbing equipment appeared; a device that is so omnipresent today that most rock climbers carry over thirty of them on their harnesses when they climb. The humble karabiner originating in Germany was originally called Karabinerhaken, which was a more general term for the spring of a carbine or the trigger mechanism on a gun.

Although most sources cite Otto Herzog as the inventor of the rock climbing karabiner in 1910, it was used in other industries before that. Instead maybe Pelton[25] should be credited with its invention since he patented the general shape way back in 1868. Whilst his version was not specific to climbing or for use with a rope necessarily, the shape and function are similar except for the gate which opened outwards. Later another inventor, A Moritz patented a snap hook for use with a rope in 1897 which was very like our modern karabiners. Most early designs had a 'snap gate' which was only held shut by a small spring but another patent was lodged the year before Moritz' by O Fechner[26] for a gate locking mechanism for a safety hook.

---

25 Peltons Patent -

http://patentpending.blogs.com/patent_pending_blog/2005/05/early_ca rabiner.html

26 Mortiz and Pelton Patents -

http://patentpending.blogs.com/patent_pending_blog/2005/06/carabin ers.html

Mountaineering specific equipment was becoming more easily available and written material was produced explaining the necessary skills of using of an ice-axe for cutting steps and securing climbers with just a rope. This shows that climbers were also developing skilful use of the hardware to help keep them safe and passing that knowledge on through literature. These techniques of step cutting and utilising a rope for safety are so fundamental to climbers that they are still employed today.

The final years of the Golden Age of mountaineering were the three decades that led up to the First World War. Oscar Eckenstein was a character whose contribution in this period was more than the redesigning of the crampon, his name crops up in many areas. He organized one of the first climbing competitions[27], when he got some locals to compete for a cash prize whilst in the Karakoram in 1892. This was a bouldering competition and it was in bouldering that Oscar had some great ideas and used them as part of a 'masterclass' session teaching people about balanced climbing movement. Heading out to the Greater Ranges in 1902, Eckenstein and another mountaineer attempted what was to become known as K2 and reached 6700m before a series of mishaps turned them back. His partner for the climb was an intriguing chap called Aleister Crowley. As we are about to find out, he was something of a chameleon when it came to life and he lived up to his other name 'The Beast'.

---

27 Whilst I say the first competition, I think we as mountaineers are fooling ourselves if we believe that there wasn't competition in the mountains, take Whymper's victorious shouts down and trundling a boulder at the Italians he 'beat' to the summit of the Matterhorn. Even before that the cash prize offered for the first ascent of Mont Blanc, certainly makes for a motivation beyond that of being the first to succeed.

Born in Royal Leamington Spa, Crowley had a strict religious father who would read verses from the bible at breakfast. Aleister was only eleven when his father died and he inherited his fortune. He was expelled from at least one of his schools and despised most of the others. Eventually he ended up at Cambridge where he started to engage more with mountaineering and made at least one trip a year to the Alps between 1894 and 1898. He was recognized by his peers as a 'promising but somewhat erratic climber'[28].

As well as being an accomplished mountaineer and climber[29], Crowley was an occultist, a chess player and an outspoken bisexual who sired more children than the average guest of Jeremy Kyle or Jerry Springer. He also used drugs to reach enlightenment and to have other pseudo-religious experiences in one of the many cults he was in or indeed set up. Despite being an habitual drug user, he still managed to maintain a meticulous record of his experiences with opium, cocaine, hashish, cannabis, alcohol, ether, mescaline, morphine and heroin. He was

---

28 This and much of this section come from one of the many biographies about Crowley, in particular Symonds, John (1997). The Beast 666: The Life of Aleister Crowley. London: Pindar Press. ISBN 978-1899828210. There's a link here to his Wikipedia entry http://en.wikipedia.org/wiki/Aleister_Crowley

29 Aleister Crowley also rock climbed, and was most famed for his explorative climbs on the rotting chalk cliffs of Beachy Head, where he climbed among other routes the 'Devil's Chimney' in 1897, which he required being rescued from by local peasants who goaded Crowley as they saved him. He laid a curse on the local of Eastbourne promising "all hell, fire and brimstone would befall the town of Eastbourne", when the tower collapse, which it did back in 2001.

also considered a racist and somewhat of a misogynist.

In spite of this, he has figured in popular culture mainly because he lived his life with a simple motto, '*Do what thou wilt*'. In the 1908 book *The Magician* by W S Maugham, the lead character was based on Crowley as were fictional characters in several other books. He features on the iconic album cover of Sgt Pepper's Lonely Heart Club Band where he is situated between Sri Yukteswar Giri and Mae West. Jimmy Page from Led Zeppelin owned some of his artefacts and bought a house Crowley had owned on the banks of Loch Ness in Scotland. The Doors posed on the back cover of their Album 13 with a small bust of him. Ozzy Osbourne wrote a song called 'Mr Crowley' and Iron Maiden's Bruce Dickinson wrote a screenplay based on *The Magician* called Chemical Wedding.

In 1905, Crowley set out to India to attempt Kanchenjunga which at the time was considered to be the tallest mountain in the world. On this trip, Crowley appeared to his team to be so reckless that they mutinied on the mountain. Crowley suggested that they wait for better conditions before descending because they had been turned back to Camp 5 by an avalanche higher up. Some of the team carried on down and were swept away by another avalanche, their deaths contributing to Kanchenjunga's reputation as the world's most treacherous peak. When told of this news at the high camp, Crowley simply sent one man from his team to try to help. Opting to stay in his tent seemed like a callous act and one that led to him being ostracised by the climbing establishment.

On his return to what is now Calcutta, Crowley shot dead a man who tried to mug him and was forced to leave the country. Heading to China, Crowley fell off a 40ft cliff and landed unscathed confirming his belief that he was a form of deity. He then set about establishing his own religious cults. Later in his life, Crowley was linked to Ron Hubbard, the 'founder' of the Church of Scientology. Hubbard was a reasonably well known science fiction author before writing self-help books like "Dianetics". He is most famously quoted or misquoted as saying, "If I wanted to make real money I'd start my own religion" and when he met Crowley, that is just what he did.

This period in history had seen many triumphs and tragedies in mountaineering, engineering and science. It was typified by brave men and women pioneering previously unexplored territory and served as a springboard for modern alpinism and rock climbing as a pastime. The exploration continued up until 1914 when Archduke Franz Ferdinand of Austria, the heir to the throne of Austria-Hungary, was shot dead by a Yugoslav national on the 28th June. Various Imperialist groups and policies quickly led to battle lines being drawn and one month later most of Europe was at war. Over the next four and a bit years, some 9 million people died. That sounds a lot but World War One only makes it to 6th place in the World's Most Deadly Conflicts behind three massive Chinese revolutions, Genghis Khan's Mongol conquest and of course the horrific Second World War. The death toll then included the Holocaust, which in itself killed almost as many people as the First World War. Sadly, as world powers raced to arm themselves with more destructive weapons, climbing was placed on a back burner. That arms race did spur several technological advances in materials, manufacture and design, as we shall see later when we look at the inter-War years.

In this chapter I have described the growth in the popularity of mountaineering with the upper classes and the origins of specialist equipment. The basic forms of the ice axe, crampon and karabiner appeared then and, although they have since been refined, their inventors would have no problem recognising them. They did such a good job that essentially the basic tools are still the same. I have also introduced some of the most influential climbers of those times and briefly tried to capture why I find their contributions to the foundations of the sport so fascinating. In the process, I touched on the notion that the early pioneers of mountaineering and science exposed themselves to unknown risks. I am always amazed that those mountaineers achieved so much when so little was known at the time about the affect of altitude on the body and mind and how that can profoundly alter the risks involved. So in the next chapter I look at how mountaineering and science have combined to explain the affects of altitude and arm modern   climbers with the knowledge to reduce their risks. Among other things, I question why Everest may well have only ever seen a handful of ethically pure ascents, amidst the hundreds of people who can summit over a few days now.

3 BAD ALTITUDE

As part of my Masters Degree I had to give a talk on either the physiological effects of altitude or the use of ergogenic aids, aka performance enhancing drugs. A friend had recently climbed Everest for the bio-epic 'The Wildest Dream' and had been kind enough to give me a list of the medication he had taken on his ascent. Never one to make life easy, I chose to combine the two subjects and gave a talk on why Everest may never have seen a true ascent. This is a question I confront in this chapter. In answering it, I combine my twin passions, science and mountaineering and add a historical perspective. More and more people go up Everest every year. In the two month long season of 2012, over 500 summited most of them returning safely. So my argument that only a few have ever made ethically pure ascents is contentious. I explain the complexities of the physical effects of altitude on the human body and in doing so, I tell the story of the scientists, technologists and adventurers who discovered them and the medical advances that followed.

Today much is known about what happens to the human body when living, working or playing at altitude but this was not always the case. By the end of 19th Century, mountaineers had been venturing into the high Alps for many years. They experienced the effects of altitude but thought these were the results of rancid or stagnant air in these places. And long before those observations were made by western mountaineers, the Chinese first made reference to the symptoms of what is now referred to as Acute Mountain Sickness or AMS. In a classical Chinese text from 30 BC, the Tseen Han Shoo mentioned two mountains passed over by travellers on the Silk Route and referred to them as 'Big Headache

Mountain' and 'Little Headache Mountain'.

In some cultures, people have lived at altitude for generations. The homes of some non-European indigenous communities are at heights in excess of 2500m. At this height, it is alarmingly harder to breathe than at lower altitudes for those who are unused to it. Those who live successfully at such heights have clearly acclimatised over their lifetimes to this rarefied air. It was only in more modern times that European travellers to these elevated places began to recognise that the symptoms and illnesses they experienced were caused by the altitude itself.

One of the earliest reports of the effects of living at altitude was from a mining village high in the Andes. The story was told by the Spanish who conquered most of South America and were followed by missionaries who sold their false god for gold. In the village there is a graveyard that looks like any other but, on closer inspection, this one tells a horrible tale. For the first 56 years of the conquistadors' occupation not a single pregnancy went full term. The relative lack of oxygen made it impossible for the settlers to give birth successfully and within that graveyard there is a section occupied by the bodies of the many miscarried infants.

In parts of South America mines have now been established at even greater heights, some in excess of 5000m. Amongst the workers there is a strange phenomenon; the majority of their babies are conceived on the same weekend. Although they are certainly acclimatised to function at this altitude, the effect of prolonged exposure to living at 5000m is so extreme that none of the men can produce enough healthy sperm on a day to day basis and they are effectively sterile for most of the year. Only when all the workers get an extended period of leave once a year and return to their family homes at lower altitudes, can they produce enough sperm of sufficient health to make the swim for conception.

The most famous accounts from the conquistadors in South America were those of Spanish Chronicler Joseph De Acosta. He published his *"The Naturall and Morall Historie of the East and West Indies"* in 1590 in which he noted the peculiar effects of being at altitude. Seventy years later, the scientist Robert Boyle read this book and decided to conduct research into atmospheric gases. By the time he completed his research, he could precisely calculate the volume of a gas at a given temperature and pressure.

A contemporary of Boyle, Italian physicist and mathematician Torricelli, was also preoccupied with investigating the atmosphere. He described the Earth as being covered by an ocean of air which has weight and therefore exerts pressure and he invented a barometer in 1644 to measure it. Armed with this theory and the barometer, another scientist, Blaise Pascal[30], measured the variation in pressure with change of height[31]. He proved

---

30 As an aside, Pascal was also something of a philosopher, and made what has become known as Pascal's Wager, which dealt with the argument of whether to believe in god or not. He posited the notion that God's existence could be argued either way, so assuming a 50/50 split in the odds if you had to wager then you need to consider what the results of wager could be. In the case of God he argued that if you bet on believing in God and win, you win everything. If however you lose as God does not exist you lose nothing, so you should wager without hesitation.

31 This is part lie, as it was his elder sister's husband Florin Perier who carried the barometer to the top of Puy De Dome, on the edge of

that pressure decreases as height increases because with less of the 'ocean' above, there is less weight pressing down. In doing so, he became so synonymous with pressure that the standard units for measuring it are called Pascals. .

Taken together, the work of Boyle, Torricelli and Pascal proved that, at the lower pressure at higher altitudes, a single breath of the same volume as at sea level actually contains less air. Their combined discoveries, made in the 16th Century before the term 'scientist' had even been coined, enabled a huge shift in thinking about the Earth's atmosphere.

The existence of Air, along with Earth, Fire and Water, as one of the four classical Elements was known to all ancient philosophies. When Boyle, Torricelli and Pascal were investigating how it exerts pressure on the planet, they thought of it as a single element. More than another century went by until, in a single scientifically momentous decade, the 1770s, several scientists contributed to a huge breakthrough in the proof that air is a combination of gases. A Scot, Daniel Rutherford, discovered nitrogen and found that it does not support life. An Englishman, Joseph Priestley and a German, Carl Scheele, independently discovered oxygen and found it to be essential for burning and respiration. The work of another Englishman, Henry Cavendish, revealed the composition of the air to be 4 parts nitrogen to 1 part oxygen although those names were not used at the time. And the French "father of chemistry", Antoine Lavoisier, had his work into the properties of the gases rudely interrupted by the French Revolution and the guillotine.

Clermont in France. Later the standard unit of pressure was named; the Pa or Pascal. Pascal also invented the first mechanical calculation machine to help his father work out taxes; he was only 19 at the time.

While scientists struggled to develop theories from their results, others were excited by a practical application of recent discoveries about gases. One of the French Montgolfier brothers, Joseph, observed hot air rising above a fire. He decided it was a new gas released by burning, declared it to have the property "levity" and modestly named it after himself. His brother Etienne, who was more of a salesman than an inventor, was recruited and the pair set about trapping the hot gas in a taffeta balloon which not only rose but lifted more than its own weight. Etienne's marketing skills and the possibility of a military use for the balloon interested King Louis XVI. But there were concerns about the potential ill effects of travelling high into the atmosphere. As yet untroubled by the spectre of the guillotine, the King generously offered to use his contacts at the Bastille to acquire prisoners as test subjects. But eager volunteers made this unnecessary and the Montgolfiers' most successful early flight in 1783 carried three people to a height of 910m, landing 9km away after 25 minutes.

In that same year however, a competing technology, the gas balloon, was spectacularly more successful. Using Henry Cavendish's method for isolating hydrogen gas which is lighter than air, Jacques Charles used it to fill a balloon which carried him to a height of 3000m over a 2 hour trip of 36km. Public enthusiasm for ballooning was huge. Thousands of tickets for trips were sold. And some passengers experienced firsthand the effects of altitude on the human body. They suffered from severe hypoxia; lack of oxygen in the blood. That the condition was not understood and did not have a name was irrelevant to those poor souls for whom it proved fatal.

Only three years later, in 1786, Balmat and Paccard made their equally important but far slower ascent to a much greater height than even the most successful of the early balloonists. They made the first ascent of Mont Blanc and stood on its 4810m summit. The embryonic sport of mountaineering was born. Other climbers followed their example and many more achieved higher peaks than ever before. Gradually, their combined experiences made it clear that being at greater altitude produced a 'Mountain Sickness'. They described the particular symptoms; a lassitude that at times utterly incapacitated them preventing even the slightest exertion, headaches, difficulty breathing, feverishness, quickening of the heart, nausea and sometimes vomiting.

A further century passed before the science existed to explain 'Mountain Sickness' in terms of the changes in processes within the body caused by large alterations in pressure. French politician and physiologist Paul Bert published his investigation into the effects of abnormally higher and lower air pressures on living creatures in 1878. Of specific interest to mountaineers was his discovery that exposure to the lower pressures at high altitudes results in lower levels of oxygen in the blood. But the actual impetus for his research was the remarkable ambition of the engineers of the time who needed workers to be able to endure desperately hazardous conditions.

Paul Bert's research into the physiological effects of pressure changes developed from studying 'caisson disease', usually called the 'bends' or decompression sickness nowadays. Several engineering projects, for example the construction of the main stone supports of the Brooklyn Bridge in New York, required workers to labour underwater in pressurised caissons. A caisson was an open box placed upside down on the river bed, the water being pumped out and replaced with air. Inside, the workers dug down into the mud and the box sank as they worked until they found a suitably solid foundation. To keep the water from flooding the cavity they had to keep the pressure within higher than normal. During the construction, 600 people were involved with the caisson work and 110 cases of decompression sickness were recorded. Some of these were fatal or caused serious injury to the workers, including the bridge designer's son Washington Roebling. Washington became project manager but after developing a severe case of the bends he too almost lost his life and was no longer able to visit the site.

The potential of Paul Bert's work as a basis for research into Mountain Sickness was clear and in the 1890s, a decade after it was published, two high altitude 'laboratories' were established. One was the Vallot hut which now serves as an emergency refuge just below the summit of Mont Blanc. The other was built with the support of Queen Margherita of Savoy on Monte Rosa. Named in her honour, the Capanna Regina Margherita is still used for valuable high altitude research by Italian physicians. A keen and competent alpinist, Margherita made the ascent to 4559 metres to visit the hut shortly after it was opened. She would probably have been appalled that she is remembered today less for her contribution to mountaineering achievement and more for the basic cheese and tomato pizza.

At the Vallot hut, one of the researchers died of what is retrospectively believed to have been the first recorded case of High Altitude Pulmonary Oedema (HAPE) and an autopsy indicated that the illness was a direct result of living at altitude. The Vallot team, who were the subjects of their own research, found that after a period of time they experienced what they described as a 'ventilatory acclimatisation' or an automatic breathing response to altitude. The work of these two laboratories made the first steps into the science that has become high altitude physiology and medicine. They provided a springboard for later research expeditions to the highest peaks which focussed on the specific causes of changes in the body at altitude.

One such research expedition, led by John Scott Haldane, took place only thirty years after the laboratories in the Alps were established. This Scottish physiologist was a world authority on dangerous gases. Already responsible for coalminers using canaries as an early warning system and the decompression tables that helped deep sea divers, World War I prompted his invention of the first gas mask and he would go on to invent the oxygen chamber. So far reaching were the findings of Haldane's 1910 expedition to Pike's Peak that they are still applied by modern mountaineers and athletes. And so thorough was the experimental design that it provides the model for research in this area even now, more than a century later.

Firstly, Haldane chose a location for the study and decided it should be

'*a nice, comfortable mountain*'

because to reach the Capanna Margherita or the Valot Hut,

'*one must climb several thousand feet over snow and ice …the climate is arctic even in midsummer …worst of all the investigators must cook for themselves*'[32].

At the time, the actual ascent to these first laboratories was seen by many, including Haldane, as a confounding variable that limited the research. In fact, Haldane quipped in a letter to a fellow expedition member that observed effects might be due as much to bad cooking by the scientists, as to the altitude. In the Rocky Mountains, Pike's Peak provided a respectably high summit at 4302m,

---

32 This was recounted by Henderson, the other leader in the Pike Peaks expedition in his article. Life At Great Altitudes in the Yale Review 1914.

a cog railway to the top and a hotel in which the researchers and their subjects could live in comfort to eliminate an arduous ascent or arctic living conditions as variables.

The second important element of the experimental design was the collection of data. The scientists had identified observable physiological changes in the human body caused by altitude and prepared to collect separate data for each one. Amongst their comprehensive battery of tests they measured; the composition and quantities of gases in the alveoli or air sacs of the lungs, partial pressures of oxygen and carbon dioxide in the blood, changes in periodic breathing and estimates of changes in blood circulation rates. The measurements were all made repeatedly over an extended period so that differences caused by variations in altitude could be monitored.

The third important aspect of the design of the experiment was that data were collected over three consecutive five week periods; before travelling to the summit, whilst living at altitude and immediately after returning to sea level. Crucially for the future of high altitude physiology and medicine, this allowed   both acclimatisation and de-acclimatisation, to be precisely quantified. Subsequent studies have recreated the same experiment over five week acclimatisation periods and identified many more of the effects of ascending to and staying at high altitudes. These have particularly benefitted mountaineers. But Haldane's research into de-acclimatisation is almost unique and has provided what are still some of the best sets of data available to explain the benefits, especially for world class athletes, of training at altitude and competing at lower venues.

By the time Haldane completed his research mountaineers had already been to   altitudes considered extreme at the time. The three highest peaks identified by the 1856 Great Trigonometric Survey of British India were called the "Himalayan Giants"; Kangchenjunga, K2 and Everest. The few attempts to climb any of these had failed and there was doubt that it was even possible. One Dr Kellas wrote a letter to the Royal Geographic Society in May of 1916 which was entitled 'A Consideration of the Possibility of Ascending the Loftier Himalaya'. He covered diverse issues including the value of expeditions for scientific research and making more accurate surveys. But essentially he was intent on convincing this influential organisation that man must conquer and investigate every spot on earth.

In setting out an answer to his own question, Kellas selected evidence from recent achievements and scientific findings. He cited manned balloon flights which, all this time after the Montgolfier brothers had gone to Heaven by the more usual route, were being used extensively for meteorology and general adventuring. Famously, Frenchman Gaston Tissandier had escaped from Paris in his balloon when the city was besieged during the Franco-Prussian War. Later, in 1875, his return from a record breaking flight to 8600 m had been less joyful than he had hoped for; both his passengers had perished. Just after the turn of the new century, Polish balloonist Arthur Berson and meteorologist Reinhard Süring had achieved a height of 10 800 m. The supplementary oxygen they had taken from 6000 m did not prevent their falling unconscious at 10 000 m. They regained consciousness and had eventually returned safely but it must have been hard for Kellas to put a positive spin on it. In fact, he conceded that on this evidence mountaineers were no more likely to be able to go any higher in a healthy state than the balloonists had. The Society members reading Kellas' letter would have realised immediately that the altitude safely reached by the highest balloon flights was some way below the highest summits. Perhaps the greatest peaks were beyond reach.

Then Kellas dropped into the letter his carefully primed bombshell. Armed in part with Haldane's research, he pointed out the importance of the recently identified process of 'acclimatising'. He emphasised that the gradual approach of mountaineers to higher altitudes gave them time to 'acclimatise'. At the highest altitudes, he argued, supplementary oxygen could be used as it had been on recent balloon trips. Kellas now proposed that an ascent of Mount Everest would be possible with a combination of acclimatisation and oxygen enriched air to breathe on the upper reaches of the mountain.

Kellas then took his readers much further. After reviewing the results of experiments on the use of air chambers, he came up with a visionary prediction, so far ahead of its time that it would be some 70 years before it would be tested;

"It follows, therefore, from experiments in air-chambers that the ascent of Mount Everest should be quite possible without adventitious aids, agreeing with observations of balloonists. Again however the conditions are not comparable, since the subject in an air chamber cannot become acclimatised to low oxygen pressure, whereas the mountaineer can".

Kellas had brought together all the available science and made the case that it would be possible to climb the world's highest mountains. With that statement of belief, the move towards an expedition to stand on the roof of the world began.

In the century that has passed since Haldane's Pike's Peak Expedition, more research has refined knowledge of the process of acclimatisation. Better technologies for making physiological measurements have become available and high altitude medicine has contributed to and benefitted from advances in other areas of research into human physiology. So the body's responses to working and living at extreme altitudes can be explained, anticipated and managed much more precisely.

The 'ocean' of atmosphere which surrounds the Earth is stretched from sea level to its outer margins at about 100km. Densest at sea level, half of all the air on the planet is in a layer only about half a kilometre deep and it thins out rapidly as height increases. In fact, air pressure decreases exponentially with altitude although the proportion of oxygen remains at about one fifth. So the amount of oxygen available to breathe at an altitude of 5000m is half that available at sea level and at 8000m it falls to one third. This means that at altitude humans can slowly start to suffocate, indeed a person instantly transported from sea level to the summit of Everest would essentially asphyxiate in minutes[33]. For me this raises two questions. Firstly, what are the physiological effects of surviving with so little oxygen? And secondly, when almost all the people who have summited the tallest mountains in the world have used supplementary oxygen, why is it that a few can do so without it?

Acclimatisation is the term for the series of physiological changes triggered in the body by oxygen deprivation. Altitude research has tracked those responses when the human body is exposed to the rarefied air at altitude. The shortage of oxygen is quickly detected by chemical receptors in the arteries which set off an automatic response to increase breathing and heart rate. This response not only speeds up breathing and heart rate but also increases the amount of air breathed in with each breath and the volume of blood pumped with each heartbeat.

---

33 This is somewhat a proved hypothesis through those early ballooning accidents.

After a while, the increased efficiency in breathing and heart patterns causes hyperventilation and the blood becomes alkaline. The alkalosis triggers a response in the kidneys, where bicarbonate is taken from the blood stream and excreted in urine in an attempt to re-acidify the blood. As a knock-on effect of this chemical reaction, the kidneys remove some water from the blood which is transferred to the bladder and passed out as urine. This too has a beneficial effect; the blood thickens and concentrates the oxygen-carrying red blood cells.

As the body gets rid of all that fluid it begins to dehydrate. The problem of dehydration is exacerbated by the altitude. As well as less oxygen in the air, there is also less water vapour. In the drier atmosphere, more water than usual evaporates from the lungs with every breath. The result is that dehydration can occur quickly especially if the mountaineer is suffering from vomiting that can be associated with Acute Mountain Sickness. The problem is so critical that some alpine mountaineers use the maxim 'hydrate or die'.

By increasing the breathing and heart rate and the subsequent response in the kidneys the body adapts to carry on operating at altitude and we will stay like this for about a week to ten days at height. If we stay longer than this and the body has even more tricks up its sleeve to cheat the oxygen deprivation.

In that week the bone marrow has been slowly changing bringing erythropoietin receptors closer to the blood supply as if waiting for a signal. That signal, the hormone erythropoietin, comes from the kidneys. Binding with the receptors, it sets the body's red blood cell factory, the bone marrow, into overdrive creating many more red blood cells. The haemoglobin in those cells combines with oxygen so, at this point in the adaptation process, far more of the available oxygen can be transported to the muscles. Athletes exploit this effect with altitude training to force their bodies to create more red blood cells so that they can perform harder for longer when competing at lower altitudes. There is much debate within the athletics community about the benefits of training high and sleeping low, training low and sleeping high or training high and sleeping high. This basically comes down to whether an athlete can train effectively at altitude or whether just sleeping there is enough to get the performance enhancing effects.

Erythropoietin has been synthesised since 1983 to treat people who are chronically hypoxic because of kidney disease, anaemia and other conditions. Going by the street name of EPO, this is what most of the cyclists who were busted during the infamous 1998 Tour Du France were taking[34]. Synthesised EPO is so close to the naturally produced hormone that it is almost impossible to detect. It was only a veritable truck full of the stuff in teams' support vehicles that resulted in the Tour du France bust. So common and widely accepted was its use that many of the cyclists on the tour threatened to pull out of the event as a result.

Other than catching competitors red-handed, the only way the World Anti-Doping Association had of detecting its use was to determine the athletes' red blood cell counts. However, the instrument used to do this is cheap compared to the associated cost of doping and it is extremely easy for athletes to do themselves. So all they

---

34 It was also one of the drugs Lance Armstrong denied doping on until it became undeniable. In fact its use was so common in top level cycling that most of the winners of the Le Tour over a ten year period have at some point been implicated in its use.

have to do is find and maintain a level below that limit and they are laughing, to a point. That point being that there is a very serious side to EPO doping which is why the drug is banned from athletics and other sports. Its use or, more accurately, abuse has been linked to inducing strokes and heart attacks because it thickens the blood. Clearly those involved in high altitude mountaineering must run the same risks, although being struck down with one of those might be the least of their worries high on an alpine face.

After the natural EPO response which kick starts the production of red blood cells, the body is pretty well adapted to living, working and climbing at altitude. However there are a few more changes that have been observed in the bodies of people who have spent a long time at altitude, and that is the wasting away of body tissue, typically in the muscles and the lungs.

Everyone who spends more than a week at altitudes of more than 4000m loses weight. There is much research into and debate about the reasons for this. Nutritional deprivation is the obvious culprit and some research has shown to help combat the reduction in oxygen the body does suppress the digestive system. Digesting food needs a lot of oxygen and using up the body's reserves is a more efficient use of the limited amount available. But this is probably not the whole story since a disproportionate amount of the weight lost comes from muscle mass. Similarly, the capillaries in the lungs move closer to the alveoli, the tiny air sacs, where oxygen is transferred into the blood stream and carbon dioxide is moved out. Both of these changes make the transfer of gases and energy easier as they have less far to travel between the blood and the cells in muscles and blood and the alveoli in the lungs, scientist have yet to understand why this happens.

Acclimatisation, the physiological changes triggered by

oxygen deprivation, can be summarised as increased breathing and pulse rates, thicker blood with many more red blood cells and a degree of tissue wastage. A fully acclimatised person can survive in conditions where every breath provides only about one third of the oxygen available at sea level, which is proof of the human body's seemingly miraculous ability to adapt to hostile environments.

There are of course down sides to being at extreme altitudes or to trying to acclimatise too quickly. It is recommended that beyond 2500m the rate of ascent should not exceed 500m per day. This means it should take 7-9 days to climb to the top of Kilimanjaro at 5900m but many adventure holiday companies advertise 5-day guided trips. Cynical mountaineers, who see the ascent as little more than a glorified sponsored walk, sometimes call the mountain Killer Man Jaro and for good reason. As a result of poor acclimatisation, Kilimanjaro and many other peaks for that matter see many tourists come down with the whole array of high altitude illness. In ascending order of seriousness, these are; Acute Mountain Sickness (AMS), High Altitude Pulmonary Oedema(HAPE) and High Altitude Cerebral Oedema(HACE).

AMS is typified by headaches, nausea or vomiting which can be severe enough to immobilise the victim. If the sufferer could not move independently, this would be very problematic since the easiest and most effective treatment is to descend immediately and rapidly. Otherwise oxygen therapy or a hyperbaric chamber, aka 'Gamow bag'[35], would be necessary but probably not

---

35 A Gamow Bag, is a large inflatable bag in which the victim is placed and either a foot or motorised pump maintains a higher than ambient pressure. Effectively this reduces the altitude of the person suffering from some form of altitude related illness.

available on a small expedition.

HAPE is more serious than AMS but it is not a more serious form of the same thing. Either HAPE or HACE can be contracted straight away. High Altitude Pulmonary Oedema is a killer. Make no mistake about it, a victim is on borrowed time and must descend or be helped or carried down. Alternatively, some form of treatment in the form of Dexamethazone or supplementary oxygen can help. HAPE is the leaking of fluid into the lungs, often called 'The Bubbles' due to the bubbling sound breathing makes in the chest. Without treatment, death will follow quickly as the fluid fills the lungs and the sufferer essentially drowns.

High Altitude Cerebral Oedema (HACE) is even worse as fluid starts to leak into the brain of the victim and the pressure builds. Unconsciousness soon follows with death not far behind. The treatment again is descent, supplementary oxygen, the drug Nifedipine and luck!

At high altitude, most people experience at least the discomfort of headaches and nausea. Fortunately, most do not contract AMS, HAPE or HAPE especially if they have taken enough time while ascending to acclimatise which is the first and easiest way to avoid getting ill. Recently though a series of randomly controlled double blind trials[36] showed that some medications prescribed as treatments can be used preventatively. So more and more people are

---

36 The best test of the effectiveness of a medication is the randomly controlled double blind trial. There is both a treatment group and a control group and the random double blind bit comes from the fact that neither the researcher nor the subject knows whether the medication or the placebo is being taken. This way the study tests the effect of the medicine against the placebo effect or researcher bias.

relying on pills to avoid having to spend the time acclimatising, to alleviate uncomfortable mild symptoms and to prevent the onset of serious illness.

When carrying out drug trials for altitude medicines, what the researchers need is a group of willing volunteers, who have in the past suffered from clinically diagnosed HAPE. At the very least, that means they are stupid and did not acclimatise properly or they are from the group of unlucky people who may be genetically or physiologically predisposed to not acclimatising fully. Somehow the scientists must get about 20 or 30 of them to sign consent forms and then fire them from the valley floor to an alpine hut at 3000m in about 30 minutes. Half the group take a placebo whilst the other half is given the real drug. Both the subjects and the researchers are blind as to whether the real drug or placebo has been administered. Then all the investigators have to do is sit back and wait for up to 24 hours to see if the guinea pigs either keel over or survive. If their lungs start bubbling, the doctors have to send them rapidly back down in the cable car to hospital to see if x-rays show they have HAPE again.

The results of the double blind trials are quite staggering because Diamox, Dexamethazone and Nifedipine have all been shown to dramatically reduce the occurrence of HAPE in people who have previously suffered from the condition. This has led to a massive increase in the use of all three drugs as preventative medication. Diamox is by far the most common and it helps to speed up acclimatisation by helping the bicarbonate feedback loop in the kidneys. As a result, many tourists are regularly prescribed it for Himalayan travel. It also reduces sleep apnoea, the stopping of breathing during sleep which is characterised by a sudden gasp for air that usually wakes the sufferer. And it shows a positive benefit for the saturation of oxygen in the blood.

However, recently Dexamethazone and Nifedipine are more commonly prescribed to wannabe Everest climbers to take as a preventative instead of for their more on-label use as a cure for HAPE and HACE.

The extreme altitude that any Everest climber faces makes the air so thin that the chances of serious acclimatisation problems are much greater. In the last twenty years, Everest is no longer a mountain for the dedicated mountaineer, instead it has become little more than an extreme guided walk, with more than 500 people a year trying to summit. Very few are mountaineers and all have paid a premium to reach the summit. Inevitably someone drops down with some form of altitude related illness but the Everest baggers' moral compass appears to break at above 6000 metres and rather than stop to help, they will instead step over or around the body where it lies.

Competitive guiding companies use summit success rates to market their services. This has led to the routine use of the three high altitude drugs described here. What this means is that very few people in the last few years can claim to have ascended the world's highest peak unassisted by drugs. In fact it begs the question of what is an ethically clean ascent? At the very least, most ascentionists use supplementary oxygen and breathe concentrations equivalent to those at much lower altitudes. Effectively, they administer enough extra oxygen to lower the mountain by 1500m in real terms.

The other issue worth pondering as to whether Everest has ever actually had a truly ethical ascent is that of drug use. In a talk at the Llanberis Mountain Film Festival, I used the points above to argue that Everest has had a maximum of a handful of ascents if any at all. At the end of the talk I was accosted by a friend of Peter Habeler. In 1978 Peter Habeler accompanied Reinhold Messner on the first ascent of Everest without the use of supplementary oxygen. So they are prime candidates for the first, and possibly only, ethically pure ascent.

However there had been no declarations about any medication they took during the climb. Habeler's friend subsequently emailed him and he confirmed that they had used aspirin and sleeping pills. Now research into the use of aspirin at altitude has shown that it can help performance, probably by counteracting headaches and the thickening of the blood. But it does not alter the physiological adaptation to altitude in that it has no statistically significant effect on blood oxygen. There have been no double blind tests to see if aspirin can help prevent HAPE but it is not one of the World Anti-Doping Agency's banned substances. I was unable to determine whether their sleeping pills are banned by the WADA but they had decided not to take Diamox which is. So I feel I can say that to my knowledge Habeler and Messner have made one of the most ethically pure ascents of Everest. Messner states his ethics in his great article 'Murder of the Impossible'[37] and clearly he and Habeler refused to compromise. The Everest they climbed was not the lower summit achieved by those who are pulled up by guides and pushed up by sherpas whilst sucking on oxygen and popping pills.

What I have found interesting about the study of altitude is that historically discoveries in many other fields of science or technology occurred outside the realm of mountaineering. These were eagerly embraced by climbers and used to push forward the boundaries of what is

---

37 Reinhold Messner first published this article in 1971 in Mountain – 15. Someone has re-published it on the internet at the link below.

http://upwardtrail.multiply.com/journal/item/1/The_Murder_of_the_Im possible

possible. Research at altitude on the other hand has required the participation of mountaineers to occur at all. So it seems only right that the results are useful in the sphere of climbing.

The principal purpose of research at altitude, since Queen Margherita opened one of the first laboratories high on Monte Rosa, has been to advance medical practice. Knowledge of how the body can be helped to cope with low oxygen levels, hypoxia, is crucial for treating diseases of the heart, lungs, kidneys and trauma. The hypoxic state of the subjects on research expeditions at altitude is what makes them great guinea pigs for modelling the oxygen levels found in trauma victims. Physiologists have produced a lot of high altitude science which has been reverse engineered to help doctors in accident and emergency departments to treat trauma victims with low levels of blood oxygen. It is why ambulances and mountain rescue teams use oxygen to treat trauma victims and, more recently, why the London Air Ambulance is taking blood and a doctor trained in transfusion on call outs to help people who have suffered serious injuries by restoring higher levels of blood oxygen as soon as possible.

One of the most prestigious research expeditions of recent times has been the first Caudwell Xtreme Everest Expedition in 2007. Using Everest as the most extreme high altitude laboratory in the world, a team of mountaineering intensive care specialists, anaesthetists, researchers into critical illnesses and volunteers used themselves as subjects. One particularly phenomenal observation was made during an experiment at 8400m, in what is commonly referred to as the 'death zone'[38].

---

38 The death zone was popularised by Jon Krakauer in 'Into Thin Air', since then it has been used by many media outlets to add hype and

In a physiology lab transported up to the South Col, the Caudwell team put a fellow researcher on an exercise bike for a test. During it they recorded the lowest ever saturation of blood oxygen in any living human; a staggering 54%. In a healthy human at sea level this reading would normally be around 90-100% and a reading in the mid 80s would give serious cause for concern. As a result, this figure is mind-blowing because the researcher was not in the process of dying but was actively exercising at altitude, which perhaps shows that a fully acclimatised human can adapt to life in the 'death zone'. Possibly the 8000m threshold of the death zone is not an absolute limit.

Another of the Caudwell Xtreme studies especially relevant and interesting here included using 208 volunteers who trekked to Everest Base Camp at 5364m to find out whether there is a genetic marker that can highlight those who will acclimatise better than others. Sadly after years of searching the data they collected, the research into the area of genetics is still inconclusive. However, the homes of 140 million of the population of our planet are higher than 2500m above sea level and research since 2001 with people in Tibet, Bolivia and Ethiopia has found that some of their adaptations could be due to genetic adaptations.

This brings me back to the two questions I posed earlier in this chapter. What are the physiological effects of surviving the oxygen deprivation of extreme altitude? When most of those who reach 8000m summits use

---

hyperbole to Everest. The fact that several people have made ascents of the highest peaks (8000m+) without supplementary oxygen as well as the results of the experiment I describe, debunk the myth that there is a line of altitude above which we cannot survive. Instead acclimatization and individual differences dictate the limit.

supplementary oxygen, why can a few do without it?

I have detailed those physiological effects and the acclimatisation process as they are currently understood. However ongoing research worldwide and the achievements of mountaineers who choose not to use supplementary oxygen and drugs will continue to raise ethical questions for the future. Perhaps some people are genetically predisposed to survive at altitude, but we are yet to find conclusively what exactly might cause that. Perhaps supplementary oxygen and drugs will be replaced with patient acclimatisation, good judgement and sheer determination. The 8000m ceiling which marks the notional boundary of the death zone looks less solid than it did twenty years ago. More importantly many people who may never climb a mountain will benefit from the medical advances that research into extreme altitude has developed.

For our historical perspective of mountaineering it is important to remember that all the attempts on the highest peaks prior to the First World War were made with none of the knowledge in this chapter. So when Crowley and Eckenstein attempted K2 and Kangchenjunga and Mummery died on Nanga Parbat little was known about the true risks. The lack of knowledge and uncertainty will have certainly contributed to challenges that these pioneers faced undoubtedly making them harder. When juxtaposed against the mountaineering challenges we set ourselves nowadays, we have the option of bringing the mountain down to our level or taking on the mountain on its own terms. Ethical arguments aside, the fact that Everest, the highest point on earth, is now available to almost anyone who can afford the price tag is a tribute to how we have utilised science, technology and medicine to turn one of the last great feats of human exploration into a commercial peak.

4 THE WORLD WARS AND MOUNTAINEERING

Two of the most important events in the history of climbing occurred between the World Wars. The first was the series of early attempts to scale Everest as a direct result of the preceding research into altitude. The second was the iconic ascent of the North Face of the Eiger. Taking place against the background of growing tension in Europe, The Eiger was used by the Nazi propaganda machine to strengthen its following in the build up to the Second World War. This period also saw some of the most far reaching technological and scientific advances ever achieved which have formed the foundations of modern life.

The outbreak of World War I in Europe immediately changed the Alps from playground to battlefield. When Italy joined Britain, France and Russia in fighting the German and Austro-Hungarian alliance, the mountainous barrier between Italy and Austria became a frontline. It was imperative that the passes through the Dolomites should be guarded and possession of the high ground was the key. To move troops and heavy artillery into place amongst the forbidding limestone pinnacles required determined and creative engineering. Precipitous paths with fixed cables and tunnels were hewn from the rock and connected by ladderways. They are commonly known now as 'via ferratas', the anglicisation of the Italian for 'iron ways'. As a testament to those who first constructed and used them, many of the old frontier posts and gun emplacements are still in place and some of the original equipment still protects the paths. They are maintained by the Italian Alpine Club who have refurbished many of the original military routes and established new ones.

Scrambling along these improbable ways through impressively steep cliffs and buttresses is now enjoyed by many as a recreational pursuit and most of the classic mountaineering routes in the Dolomites are accessed by via ferratas.

It should not be forgotten that in the early 1900s, the thousands of troops who built and relied upon the via ferratas had no concept of the mountains as a place for recreation. Only a minority, recruited locally and accustomed to herding animals on high summer pasture were used to the terrain. They knew better than any that the mountains were no place to be in winter. The conditions when the snows came were brutal. One Austrian officer noted,

"The Mountains in winter are more dangerous than the Italians."

In spite of ferocious fighting, it is a matter of recorded fact that the mountains killed more soldiers than ever met their deaths at the hands of their enemies.

They slipped and fell from icy paths and ladders, cut off by snow fall, they starved and froze at their posts. Over a ten day period in December 1916, around 10 000 soldiers from both sides were killed in avalanches across the region. Entire regiments were lost, their bodies not being found until the following spring. The greatest single death toll occurred on December 13th near the Marmolada, where a large avalanche wiped out an entire battalion of Austrian soldiers who were stationed below the summit of the Grand Poz. Two hundred thousand tons of snow, ice and rock tore their barracks apart and 300 soldiers lost their lives.

Avalanches were not unusual to the mountain dweller or traveller who regarded them as a variety of natural disaster to be avoided at all costs. Strabo, a Greek traveller, mentioned alpine passes in his book on Geography written in the first century BC noting that,

"these places are beyond remedy; and so are the layers of ice that slide down from above — enormous layers capable of intercepting a whole caravan and of thrusting them into the chasms that yawn below. For there are numerous layers resting on one another, because there are congelations upon congelations of snow that have become ice-like; and the congelations that are on the surface from time to time are easily released from those beneath…"

Strabo had correctly observed that layers of snow can easily be released, two key aspects of a snow slide. It was not until the 18th Century that further definitions were recorded which distinguished between ground (or slab) avalanches and airborne (or powder) avalanches. He also correctly noted that both are more likely to occur within the first 24 hours after fresh snowfall.

In mountainous areas across the world and down the ages, knowledge of common avalanche paths has been passed down through generations so that settlements and roads could be safely sited to avoid them. But in the early decades of the twentieth century, Europe was developing quickly. The railway companies, hydropower plant operators and promoters of ski tourism[39] in Switzerland supported the establishment of the Commission for Snow and Avalanche Research (SLF) at Davos. SLF researchers produced weekly snow reports for skiers, trained members of the Swiss military and made assessments to inform local government on planning decisions in mountain areas. At the end of World War II, it became the International Centre for Snow and Avalanche Research. The Centre, whose sole aim was to increase the understanding of

---

39 One of the first 'package' holidays to the Alps occurred in 1903, after the first winter tourists started heading to the Alps in 1864 where the first mechanised ski lift was developed in 1908.

avalanches, now shared its expertise with scientists from all over the world to the benefit of all who lived, worked, played or indeed fought in the mountains. It is to this day one of the few dedicated avalanche research centres in the world.

In 1939 they produced a magnum opus, '*Snow and its Metamorphism*'. This contained sections on snow crystal metamorphism, snow mechanics, the characteristics of types of terrain, test methods, snow density, temperature and radiation. In this book, a suggested method to test snow hardness was to fire a bullet into the snowpack. However, the subsequent time needed to find the bullet made this test impractical and it was quickly dropped.

Whilst perhaps less spectacular, other procedures detailed in their comprehensive work proved essential to those assessing the long term avalanche risk when siting buildings and also to climbers and mountaineers assessing the short term risk in a particular location. The risk can only be 'assessed' and not 'predicted' because to this day the prediction of avalanches is not an exact science but a judgement of the acceptability of the level of risk for an activity. The anatomy of avalanches and the conditions likely to trigger them are now much better understood by many more of the people who go into the mountains. The knowledge undoubtedly saves many lives but avalanches and the collapse of cornices and seracs are still so hard to predict that they cause many deaths every year.

In recent years, heavy snowfalls have resulted in some massive avalanches that have devastated alpine villages with tragic consequences. On these occasions, the 'rulebook' just did not apply as a chain of unforeseen, abnormal events led inexorably to disaster. For example, the winter of 1999 in the Chamonix valley in France saw an avalanche so powerful that it almost destroyed the village of Montroc and so rare that the avalanche track had been inactive for 91 years.

In the days before February 9th, an unprecedented 2 to 3 metres of snow had built up on the opposite side of the valley, on the Grand Montets side. The mountain was closed to skiers because of the extreme avalanche risk. The snow continued to become deeper and heavier and more and more unstable. Just before 2.40pm, unusually strong gusts of wind released the unstable snow and a rare form of airborne avalanche careered down the mountain at over 100mph. It crossed the main road and a river at the base of the valley before carrying on for another 100m up the opposite side. It bulldozed 3 chalets, damaged 15 others and killed 12 people. All those buildings were believed to be in a 'safe zone', and the tragedy illustrates that, despite having a growing understanding of avalanches and their usual paths, freak 100 year events, like that in Montroc, still cannot be predicted.

The Swiss, a nation largely untouched by either of the World Wars, dominated research into avalanches. Throughout the rest of Europe unsurprisingly, the military imperatives of war were spurring on the development and spread of other technologies. One that was in its infancy at the start of World War I was transformed by its end into the dominant form of communication. Its complex story exemplifies the tensions between science and business. The technology is radio of course.

The name of the Italian entrepreneur, Gugliemo Marconi, has become practically synonymous with radio. Yet he arguably invented very little but astutely cashed in on others' discoveries. The story of radio actually starts way back with Thomas Edison. He famously invented a viable light bulb but in 1891, he also successfully patented a means to transmit electrical signals. It was however British physicist Oliver Lodge who sent the first radio message during a lecture at Oxford University. For the most part Lodge is unheard of in science because of some very unfortunate timing. After he had proved the existence of the electro-magnetic waves predicted by the theory of Scottish mathematician James Clark Maxwell, he felt overworked and decided to postpone the announcement until he got back from a holiday. As a result, Heinrich Hertz beat him to it, going down in history as the first to demonstrate transmission of electro-magnetic waves. But in 1894, Lodge gave a lecture on 'The Work of Hertz'. Using a simple device he had made for the demonstration, he showed his audience how, when he pressed a button in one circuit, a bell rang in another totally unconnected circuit. Momentously, this was the first transmitted and received wireless message but the unassuming Mr Lodge is still almost unknown.

The race was on to take this emerging technology further. Amongst the many working on it, two of the most influential were Marconi and Jagadish Chandra Bose. As a businessman, Marconi was intent on finding a viable commercial use for radio. In stark contrast, the altruistic Indian scientist Bose shared and published a steady stream of his work, mostly unpatented, purely in the interests of science.

Under the Raj, Bose had battled against racial prejudice to become a professor at the University of Calcutta. Having recreated Lodge's device for receiving radio waves, he discovered the iron-filing receiver was unreliable in the humid climate of India. Instead, he found that a semiconducting crystal in conjunction with a coiled spring was more effective at detecting radio waves. He was eventually persuaded to patent the crystals he used which were not only more efficient receptors but, most importantly, they later enabled voice messages to be broadcast and received.

Marconi on the other hand had no scientific background. Instead, he took the ideas of others and put them together to make his own radio. In the UK, he cleverly put his apparatus in a box and applied for and was awarded a patent for his 'radio box'. On receiving the patent, he revealed that the contents of the box were far from original, being based on the original work of Lodge and Bose. Patent claims were brought against him in UK courts but these were ruled in his favour. In the more stringent US courts, Marconi had to buy Edison's patent to avoid prosecution in one case and, in at least one of several other cases, the Supreme Court ruled against him stating,

"It is now held that in the important advance upon his basic patent Marconi did nothing that had not already been seen and disclosed."

Marconi however, not only went on to make his fortune in wireless technology, in 1909, he was awarded the Nobel Prize for Physics!

Climbers in North Wales have a closer connection with the history of radio than most perhaps realise. The local climbing wall, the Beacon, operated in one of Marconi's original wireless transmitting stations on the edge of Snowdonia from 1994 to 2012. The large complex building and equipment were built in 1914 and sent messages across the Atlantic during the First World War. On September 22nd 1918, successful contact was made with Australia and with that, global communication started to speed up. The station was a key piece of the world wide radio network for a quarter of a century until it was dismantled in 1939. By the end of the World War II, a new era had begun. World news could be broadcast to a wireless radio in almost every home. Of course, over the following 50 years the equipment needed to hold a conversation with someone on the other side of the planet has shrunk from the size of a factory to that of the mobile phone. But those huge transmitter stations made the world seem a smaller place and changed forever the way people thought about its possibilities.

A whole host of new technologies were slowly transforming the lives of ordinary people. By the end of the First World War cameras, telephones, typewriters and sewing machines were commonplace. Travel by public rail and road transport within national boundaries was possible for all and many travelled abroad by sea. Then back in 1908 Henry Ford released the Model T[40], the first mass production automobile. The more people bought his cars, the more he reduced the price and, when the ten millionth rolled off the assembly line at the end of the First World War, half the cars on the roads of the United States were the Model Ts. Henry Ford had literally mobilised the middle classes and started a revolution.

The First World War brought progress in mountaineering to a halt and killed many of the best European climbers of their generation. Afterwards, expeditions in the Himalaya resumed with mountaineers undoubtedly benefitting from the technological advances of the previous two decades. In particular, the publicity afforded by the revolution in global communications proved to be a double edged sword. On the one hand, it intensified nationalistic feeling and expeditions started to become much larger and more political affairs. But

---

40 The myth is that Henry Ford said the Model T was available in any colour, 'only if it's black'. But he was talking about his assembly line which could produce a car every 93 minutes 'only if it's black', because black paint dried the quickest. Recently, when asked about the oil crisis, a Ford executive was quoted as saying, "the Stone Age didn't end because we ran out of stones!'

mountaineering did begin to get wider recognition and even made its way it into the modern Olympic Games. In the 1920s, prizes were awarded for outstanding acts of Alpinism, in a similar vein to the Piolet d'Or[41] today. The 1924 Olympic gold medal for Alpinism was awarded to the members of the 1922 British Mount Everest Expedition. Pierre de Coubertin, one of the founders of the modern Olympic Games, when presenting the medals to a representative, said;

"For the first time a gold medal is awarded for alpinism, and it is awarded to the glorious expedition to the Mount Everest. Not content with having almost succeeded, they are preparing a renewed effort to finish the ascent.

Mr. Representative of the mission, we welcome your presence for the beautiful heroism displayed. At the foot of the highest mountain in Europe, we present you and your wonderful companions with this small testimony of the admiration with which all nations have followed your journey towards the untouched peaks of the highest mountain in the world. We accompany this gesture by prayers for the completion of a work that will honour not only your country but all humanity."

The rest of the team were busy preparing for a third attempt on the mountain. George Mallory, the only member of all three expeditions, was asked by a journalist why he wanted to climb Everest. To this he gave the reply which has become immortal;

"....Because its there".

This throw away but eminently quotable remark said more about Mallory's skill in dealing with reporters than it did about the reasons why he or anyone has ever engaged

---

41 The Piolet d'Or is a golden ice axe awarded for the outstanding alpine ascent of each year.

in climbing and mountaineering[42].

It was the wish of the recipients of the first Olympic gold for alpinism that one of the medals be placed on the summit of Everest. Just months before the 2012 London Olympic Games were due to start, British Mountain Guide Kenton Cool realised that dream, by taking one of the original medals to the roof of the world. In doing so, he broke the European record for scaling Everest by making his tenth ascent of the mountain. He had already managed a 'first' a few years before; setting the world record for the highest ever tweet by sending a message from the summit on his sponsors' phone to the social media site Twitter. This achievement was prompted by Kenton Cool's sponsors but it does neatly highlight the huge gulf between the technology available to those early medallists of almost a century ago and present day summiteers. Now, every year during the two climbing seasons, a temporary mobile phone network is set up at Everest base camp so that people can phone home and keep tabs on their social networks.

Everest was identified as the highest peak in the world in 1856 by the British Survey of India. This began at the southern tip of this immense country in 1802 and, working slowly northwards, took over fifty years to complete. Peak XV, as Everest was then labelled, is in Nepal so it was necessarily measured from a distant 174km away. But painstaking checking of data had already proved accurate to the extent that the peak could confidently be confirmed as higher than Kanchenjunga, the previous contender. Final calculations took into account light refraction, barometric pressure, temperature and curvature of the

---

42 Only in the last 20 years has any serious research into people's reasons for participating in high-risk sport set out to answer this question which is the topic of our final chapter.

Earth and came up with a height of 29 000 feet exactly. Fearing that people might think that was a rounded off estimate, the surveyor promptly added two feet. Recent GPS measurements give 29 035 ft (8850m) so the first result was extremely well calculated especially when about two of those extra few feet are due to the movement of tectonic plates forcing the Himalaya skywards at an estimated 6mm a year. So Everest's height is not set in stone. Problems about which local name to give the newly confirmed highest peak on the planet were predictably avoided in those colonial times by calling it after the Surveyor General, George Everest.

The history of early attempts on Everest started in 1885 when it was first suggested that Everest could be climbed by soon to be Alpine Club president Clinton Dent in his book *Above the Snow Line*. During the next 3 decades British mountaineers and others were busy with attempts in the more accessible Karakoram region. Then came Dr Kellas' letter to the Royal Geographical Society in 1916. His familiarity with the work of leading expert on altitude, Haldane, and his conviction that Everest could be climbed persuaded some influential people. With the immediate aftermath of the First World War over, planning began in earnest for a reconnaissance expedition to find an approach to the highest mountain. Nepal was closed to westerners so a route had to be found through unknown territory in Tibet.

A doctor and mountaineer, Kellas is believed to have made more ascents above 6100 m than any of his contemporaries[43]. In particular, he made the first ascent of Sikkim. At 7128m, it was the highest peak ever to have

---

43 This and the following story comes from -

http://www.alpinejournal.org.uk/Contents/Contents_1989-90_files/AJ%201989%20207-213%20West%20Kellas.pdf been climbed at the time although this was not realised until after his death. Eminently well qualified, he was invited along with George Mallory and company when they left in 1921 to pioneer a way to the base of the northern side of the peak. What exactly happened to Kellas on that expedition is largely unknown. In earlier correspondence with Haldane's son, he had reported having auditory hallucinations which had caused him to leave his teaching job at a medical training college. Retrospectively, this might indicate schizophrenia. In any event, Kellas died unexpectedly as he approached the Tibetan village of Kampa Dzong and was buried on a hillside at a point where Everest first came into view. His was one of many tragedies surrounding Everest and his burial within sight of the mountain was seen as a moving tribute to a man who had been a key catalyst in changing attitudes towards climbing the biggest peaks.

The expedition continued and spent five months on the arduous climbing needed to overcome the barriers that guarded the approach. It was Mallory who discovered the hidden East Rongbuk glacier which finally gave them access and he wrote to his wife that he was,

"about to walk off the map".

Although ill prepared for a serious attempt to climb the mountain, Mallory and colleagues Bullock and Wheeler made it up to the North Col at 7007 metres. They returned with the information that the route up the North and the North East Ridges would be long but possible.

The success of their route finding quickly led to a second expedition in 1922 and Mallory was included in this new team whose sole purpose was to climb the mountain. After two unsuccessful bids and with the monsoon season closing in, Mallory was one of those who were fit enough and whose frostbite[44] was not too severe and they went up the mountain hoping for a clear spell to make a final effort. Significant snowfall higher up gave an early warning of the coming monsoon and, on reaching the North Col again, they realised that an avalanche was all too possible on the steep slopes below Camp IV. In Charles Granville's book '*The Assault on Mount Everest*[45]', Mallory picks up the story;

"I found the effort at each step so great that no method of breathing I had formerly employed was adequate ; it was necessary to pause after each lifting movement for a whole series of breaths, rapid at first and gradually slower, before the weight was transferred again to the other foot" ....

..."*The scene was peculiarly bright and windless and, as we rarely spoke, nothing was to be heard but the laboured panting of our lungs. This stillness was suddenly disturbed. We were startled by an ominous sound, sharp, arresting, violent, and yet somehow soft like an explosion of untamped gunpowder"*.

Each man instinctively knew what it was. Desperate struggles to escape the avalanche were useless. Mallory and close to twenty men were swept away and whilst some were lucky a few ended up being taken over a cliff of ice sixty feet high and into a gaping crevasse at its base. Seven porters died and the attempt was over.

There was one man on the Everest Expedition of 1922

---

44 Mallory was sidelined for a few days. One hand was frostbitten and his heart had a "thrill". 'The Assault on Everest' by expedition leader Brigadier General Charles Bruce recounts that when Mallory's heart was given the all clear he said; "Though I was prepared to take risk with my fingers, I was prepared to take none with my heart".

45 The 'Assault on Everest' is available as a free ebook. This account on the third attempt is on page 282: http://www.ebooksread.com/authors-eng/charles-granville-bruce/the-assault-on-mount-everest-1922-cur/1-the-assault-on-mount-everest-1922-cur.shtml

who has fallen by the way side of climbing folklore; George Ingle Finch. An outspoken Australian who had been educated in mainland Europe, Finch was an eminent chemist specialising in gases. A fellow of the Royal Society, he had developed oxygen systems for high altitude mountaineers, was a strong mountaineer himself and a natural at altitude. But he failed to fit in with the British climbing establishment.

The institutional elitism of the Alpine Club which, along with the Royal Geographical Society, organised the early Everest expeditions, was captured by prospective member Scott Russell. On his first visit he was approached by the vice-president Sydney Spencer who remarked;

"I hope your proposer told you that in addition to being the oldest mountaineering club in the world, the Alpine Club is a unique one – a club for gentlemen who climb".

Spencer then pointed out of the window at a road sweeper......

"I mean that we would never elect that fellow even if he were the finest climber in the world".

The expeditions in the twenties and subsequently were dominated by public   school, Oxbridge educated men and were led by high ranking army officers. It seems Finch was a victim of the class divide in British mountaineering at the time and his contribution is still not fully appreciated.

Initially, Finch's interest in oxygen systems was to make stoves that would operate at extreme altitude. This brought him into contact with a professor of pathology George Dreyer who stated;

"I do not think you will get up (Everest) *without it* (supplementary oxygen), *but if you do succeed you may not get down again".*

On a visit to Oxford University, Finch took part in experiments on the benefits of using supplementary oxygen in a low pressure chamber simulating an altitude of 6500m. This proved conclusively that the use of oxygen had a significant effect; it reduced his pulse rate from over 140 beats per minute to less than 100 when exercising. His results were reportedly unsurpassed nearly 90 years later in 2003[46].

This outstanding performance at simulated altitude was reported to the Everest Committee before the 1921 reconnaissance expedition on which Finch had been invited. But less than a week later he was reported as unfit by two other doctors and that invitation was revoked just weeks before departure. Many people now see this as a politically motivated decision but Finch was asked to go on the 1922 expedition; an attempt on the peak.

Another climber on the 1922 expedition was C.J. Morris who recounted Col. E.L. Strutt, the deputy expedition leader's appraisal of Finch;

"...(Finch) *had been educated in Switzerland and had acquired a considerable reputation for the enterprise and skill of his numerous guideless ascents* (many members of the Alpine Club were against ascents without guides). *Besides, he was by profession a research chemist and therefore doubly suspect, since in Strutt's old-fashioned view the sciences were not a respectable occupation for anyone who regarded himself as a gentleman. One of the photographs which particularly irritated him depicted Finch repairing his own boots. It confirmed Strutt's belief that a scientist was a sort of mechanic. I can still see his rigid expression as he looked at the picture. "I always knew the fellow was a shit" he said, and the sneer remained on his face while the rest of us sat in frozen silence"*

Less bigoted opinion must have prevailed because Finch and his oxygen apparatus went along. On the approach to the mountain there was some antagonism

---

46 'George I. Finch and his pioneering use of oxygen for climbing extreme altitudes' by J.B. West, 2003 Journal of Applied Physiology. – Much of this section on Finch is plucked from this freely available online article.

towards the use of oxygen, with Mallory referring to it as 'damned heresy'. But the second attempt on the summit was made by Finch and his partner Geoffrey Bruce using the supplementary oxygen. They climbed far faster than the others and were the first humans ever to go above 8000m. They reached 8320m. Out climbing everyone on the mountain undoubtedly put the others' backs up and their achievement was certainly downplayed by the climbing establishment who saw it as 'unsporting'. But most importantly, it changed the opinion of many about oxygen, in particular that of Mallory.

Along with his colleague Dr Dreyer, Finch had helped design the oxygen systems which are still fundamentally unchanged today. They developed recommended flow rates for working and sleeping at different altitudes which had been tested both in the lab and on the mountain. Even so, Finch, the acknowledged leading authority, was not invited back on the 1924 expedition, although he was asked to modify their oxygen equipment! It seems Finch was excluded from the expedition because of petty politics; a dispute with Arthur Robert Hinks, the secretary of the Royal Geographical Society, over the number of lectures an expedition member[47] was permitted to give.

The 1924 expedition also failed tragically of course but the crucial contribution of Finch's oxygen equipment to the eventual ascent of Everest was emphasised by the leader of the successful 1953 expedition, John Hunt, thirty years later;

"...*among the numerous items in our inventory, I would single out oxygen for a special mention... only this, in my opinion was vital to success.*"

---

47 The RGS limited the number of lectures an expedition member gave until Everest was climbed. It took 30 years, a rather draconian rule in hindsight.

Finch was never invited to go to Everest again for reasons which were political and personal and because he posed a threat to the inherent class divisions of the mountaineering establishment. However, his prowess at altitude and knowledge of the oxygen system raise an intriguing question; if Finch and Mallory had been teamed up in 1924, would they have succeeded?

The status of the 1924 attempt on Everest is perhaps difficult to appreciate from a twenty first century perspective. The pride of the British Empire had been seriously dented. In 1909, an American, Robert Peary made a (since disputed) claim to be the first to reach the North Pole. Then Norwegian Amundsen beat Scott's doomed team in the race for the South Pole in 1911. So those who sought to restore national morale and possibly gain a political and economic edge in the region[48] promptly labelled Everest 'the third pole' and hopes were centred on Brigadier-General Charles Bruce and his expedition which included Mallory again and newcomer Andrew (Sandy) Irvine.

The events that followed have been talked about by those interested in mountaineering history ever since. On the third and last attempt possible that year, Mallory opted to partner up with Sandy Irvine, less for his mountaineering skills than for his practical experience with the oxygen equipment. The pair set out early on June 8th

---

48 At the time Tibet was part of what was called the "Great Game"; the struggle for military, political and commercial dominance in central Asia between Britain and Russia which began in 1838 when Britain tried to impose a 'puppet state' in Afghanistan which has been a pawn in many other political games ever since.

and one of the supporting party, Odell, had climbed up the mountain far enough to see the pair at around 1pm. One of them was on a snowy area below the final obstacle before the summit ridge, the 'second step'. If they were on their way up, they were some 5 hours behind their own schedule. But were they perhaps on their way back from the summit? At two o'clock the weather closed in and Odell lost his view of them. They never returned and this was the last sighting of them. Whether they succeeded or failed in their summit bid before they died is still surrounded by mystery. Odell changed his statement on many occasions and there was very little evidence to suggest that either Mallory or Irvine climbed the second step and made it to the summit.

That was until 1999 when a dedicated expedition to find Mallory's body, achieved just that; he was found where he had clearly fallen from below the second step. Discovery of Mallory's remains opened several other lines of enquiry that added to the speculation about whether he had made it to the summit. Firstly, his goggles were in his pocket. This suggested he had been travelling at night when he fell. Perhaps he and Irvine had been on their way up when Odell saw them and then Mallory had fallen whilst descending in the dark. Secondly, a piece of paper containing notes on the oxygen in their cylinders suggested they had taken three bottles and not two, giving them more time for a summit attempt. Finally, a photo of Mallory's wife, who for years had suffered his love for the mountain whose Tibetan name means 'Mother Goddess of the World', was not in his possession. In letters to her and to friends he had promised to leave it on the summit as a tribute.

A film was made about Mallory's disappearance in 2010. The American climber who found Mallory's body, Conrad Anker, returned to Everest with British climber

Leo Houlding to make the bio-epic called '*The Wildest Dream*'. Using historical records and archive material, they re-enacted the events as faithfully as possible. Accordingly, they climbed the second step without the fixed ladder which usually provides protection and artificial aid for summiteers now. In doing so, Anker and Houlding proved at the very least that it would have been possible for Mallory and Irvine to do the same.

Both attempts to climb Everest had seen tragic deaths and expedition members had apparently been hunting animals near their base camp. Risking the lives of climbers and porters and killing animals were both offences in Buddhist law and the Dali Lama made the decision to close Tibet to expeditions. The ban remained until 1933 and a British team made a third unsuccessful bid using Mallory's northern route three years after it was lifted. Ironically, when the first successful ascent was made in 1953 it had to be from the south. Nepal opened its doors to the world in 1949 but the following year, the Chinese invaded Tibet and northern access was lost to mountaineers for the next three decades.

Between the World Wars, Russian, German, Italian, British and American expeditions made first ascents in the Pamirs and the Karakoram although none ascended an 8000m peak. But the public was becoming used to the immediacy of news provided by a growing media industry of radio, the press and film. Attention was shifting away from long, costly but above all *distant* expeditions in the Greater Ranges to the closer and politically charged arena of the Western Alps. 'Firsts' were by now hard to come by so those seeking challenge and recognition, and there were many, focused on the six great north faces of the highest peaks. Steep, loose and shattered, cold and icy, even in summer, these walls required daring route finding and consummate climbing skills. Those who understood knew that only the very best would succeed.

The starting pistol for the race was fired in Germany after the first World War with the founding of the then openly nationalistic and anti-semitic German and Austrian Alpine Club or Alpenverein. Membership quickly grew to 250 000, it was the largest mountaineering federation in the world. Hugely popular Bergfilme, literally 'mountain films', showed the adventures of heroes who struggled against adversity, were loyal to their homeland and loved the power of nature. These fired the imagination of young Germans who visited the Bavarian Alps in their thousands every weekend. Mountaineering as a metaphor perfectly suited the propaganda purposes of the National Socialists who seized on every success to build nationalistic fervour, a movement which had its parallel in Italy. By the thirties many eager competitors for the race were lining up; mostly ordinary, young, working Germans, Austrians and Italians, who came by train, car, even by bike to take part.

The stakes were raised, when Toni and Franz Schmid from Munich climbed the north face of the Matterhorn in 1931 and were honoured with Olympic medals the following year. Attempts were made on other north faces, not without tragic incident, but it was the north face of the Eiger which drew the most intense interest. The mile high Eigerwand towers over the cannily popularised Swiss resorts of Grindelwald and Kleine Scheidegg, with the cameras and telescopes of every tourist, journalist and film maker constantly trained on it. The Jungfau Railway, tunnelled through the mountain at the beginning of the century, even provided passengers with a view from a 'window' at a station directly onto the face. It was the perfect venue.

First up, in 1935, were two more lads from Munich, Karl Mehringer and Max Sedlmeyer. They made a good start in fine weather, reaching the height of the station on the first day. Then the great difficulty of the first rock band slowed them down and the ability of the treacherous face to generate its own weather became all too apparent as a storm broke. The route was scoured by avalanches but watchers saw the pair bivouac at around 3300m as the clouds closed in. When the storm abated two days later, the climbers, who had now spent five nights on the ice encrusted face, were nowhere to be seen. Air ace Ernst Udet flew in close, saw one frozen corpse tied to the rock and assumed his partner was buried in the snow. The bodies were irretrievable and the spot is still known as the 'Death Bivouac'.

The tragedy ratcheted up the controversy a few more notches. The Swiss Government banned further attempts and Swiss guides were officially relieved of the responsibility of rescuing climbers from the face. Both measures were largely ignored. The British mountaineering establishment publicly deplored the pollution of the noble sport by German climbers willing to sacrifice themselves for Nazi ideology. They were further outraged by the new tools necessary on unrelentingly steep north faces; attaching the rope to metal pitons or pegs hammered into the rock for protection was deemed unsporting. Alpine Journal editor Edward Lisle Strutt went so far as to call the Eigerwand,

"*an obsession for the mentally deranged*", and "*....the most imbecile variant since mountaineering first began.*"

In 1936, the Olympics were to be held in Berlin and rumour had it that several of the parties lined up to attempt the face were medal hopefuls. A German rope of two from Bavaria, Andreas Hinterstoisser and Toni Kurz, and an Austrian team, Willy Angerer and Edi Rainer began separately. Hinterstoisser breached the first rock band using a high peg runner and climbing across a blank wall aided by the tension in the rope to complete the traverse which is still called after him. Kurz followed. They removed the rope and were totally committed. When the Austrians caught up with them on the third day, a falling rock struck Angerer who suffered a serious head injury and the four were forced to retreat together in perilously deteriorating conditions. After trying and failing for hours to reverse the Hinterstoisser traverse, they made their way painfully slowly towards one of the railway tunnel 'windows'. Seeing them, a railway worker raised a rescue team but an hour later only Kurtz was left alive. Guides tried valiantly but in vain to reach him and Kurtz died slowly, hanging from an abseil rope which was too short.

The Eigerwand tragedy was followed by the majestic performance of distinctly non-Aryan Jesse Owen who won four gold athletics medals in Berlin. So it was not a good summer for the propaganda machine of the Third Reich and the cream of German climbers was exhorted to avenge the fallen comrades. Matthias Rebitsch and Ludwig Vorg tried to do just that the following year but they had to retreat from above the Death Bivouac and became the first to return safely from so high on the wall. Their cool judgement and superb mountaineering skills were not the stuff of national triumphalism of course but this pair now had an intimate and unique knowledge of the face.

The next year, the annexation of Austria by Nazi Germany was forced through by Hitler in March so the symbolic significance of the two teams attempting the Nordwand in September 1938 later came to be immense. Competitors initially, the teams' departures were separated by a day. The Austrians, Heinrich Harrer[49]   and Fritz

---

49 Heinrich Harrer wrote a history of the Eigerwand called 'The White Spider' and later the story of his escape from British internment in 'Seven Years in Tibet'.

Kasparek set off first but moved slowly since Harrer had no crampons. A day later, the Germans followed. Anderl Heckmair was vastly experienced on lesser north faces and Ludwig Vorg was on his second outing on the wall. The pair was also equipped with the new twelve point crampons bought with sponsors' money. The German team caught up with the Austrians at the edge of the Second Icefield where Heckmair, by his own account, only reluctantly agreed with Vorg's suggestion that they join up because conditions were worsening and the Austrians were dangerously slow. According to the accounts of all four, from there Heckmair led, Vorg seconded him and brought up Harrer and Kasparek. They climbed through heavy snowfall and survived the frequent avalanches sweeping over them by securing themselves with pitons. By the time they topped out, the Austrians had endured three nights on the face and the Germans two but they still had to battle down the West Flank through a blizzard to safety and Victory.

Throughout, radio reporters had been broadcasting from Kleine Scheidegg to a huge international audience. The weather had limited what they had been able to see of the climb but they marshalled 'expert' opinion and speculated freely on the rest. The mountaineers were not even safely home before claims and counter claims were being made on their behalf. Somewhere, a sub-editor was already compiling a quote which perfectly sums up the Fuehrer's message but was famously attributed to Heckmair. Since it first appeared in a piece crediting him as author whilst mis-spelling his name, it does seem unlikely Heckmair ever said;

"*We, the sons of the older Reich, united with our companions from the Eastern Border to march together to victory.*"

Ever since, the best of every generation of climbers from all over the world have found new challenges on the wall where there are now more than twenty routes. Knowledge of the face, more accurate weather forecasting and a better chance of rescue perhaps make it less forbidding but it is as steep, loose and unpredictable as ever and the last seven decades have seen 64 deaths. But there have been many astonishing Eiger 'firsts'. The face was first soloed in 1963 by Michel Barbellay in 18 hours. Welshman, Eric Jones made a solo ascent in 1981 with Leo Dickinson and his crew climbing alongside filming him. Later that year, Swiss guide Ueli Buhler managed the feat in 8 hours and 30 minutes and, in 1992, Catherine Destivelle made the first female solo ascent in 17 hours. Speed soloing has obsessed some climbers who literally run up the face against the clock. In 2008, Ueli Steck[50] climbed to the top in a staggering 3 hours 54 minutes but, not content, he re-ran it to get the time down to 2 hours 47 minutes. Many thought interest in speed soloing would fade and that Ueli's record would stand for a considerable time. But the talented alpinist Daniel Arnold, turned his attention to the 1800 metre face and recorded a time of 2 hours 28 minutes in 2011.

Remarkable though these achievements are, the fascination with the events surrounding the first ascent of the Eigerwand is undiminished. The bibliography is immense. The last film about it went on general release as recently as 2010 and the next is in the pipeline. Threads on climbing websites, like Chinese Whispers, show that the controversies still echo down through history. But the fact remains that it was truly brilliant; the most advanced climb

---

50 A film of one of Ueli Steck's record breaking solo makes the climb look easy but the climbing is hard, mixed and tenuous. A video called 'Ueli Steck – The Swiss Machine' can be found here;

http://www.youtube.com/watch?v=VUWBbepsdmY

of its time which established the modern idiom in mountaineering.

The next year, Europe descended into war and the rest of the world was to follow shortly afterwards. The giant strides made in climbing and mountaineering between the World Wars had their parallel in the advances in science and technology. With hindsight, it is not difficult to select those which were the early rumblings of developments that have proved seismic over the second half of the 20th Century. As the war between the Allies and the Axis powers strengthened its grip, paralysing so many human endeavours, the finest minds of their generation, backed up by all the resources their nations could muster were focused on initiatives which might be decisive in bringing about victory.

At the time, it was unlikely that anyone would have predicted the earth shattering future effect of the descendants of the humble mechanical calculator. It was itself an accumulation of ideas, some of them works of genius, which stretched back to the abacus. A handy piece of kit, the calculator was operated by a person who was called the computer. At some point, the name was transferred to the machine, perhaps in the late 1930s when the electronic versions were developed which were to prove crucially important in weaponry and code breaking throughout World War II. Those first computers used vacuum tube transistors based on the semi-conductors discovered by Bose, initially designed as amplifying circuits for radio and telephony. They took up massive amounts of space and drew considerable electricity to power them. Notoriously unreliable and complicated to use, they needed constant maintenance. The term 'debugging' originated then and it did not mean sorting out programming errors. It is attributed to Admiral Grace Hopper when she was on secondment to the

Massachussetts Institute of Technology. A circuit shorted out, stopping a computer working and, when the moth responsible was removed, she coined the phrase; *'debugging the system'.*

A key influence in Computer Science was the work of Alan Turing on the problems associated with sequential logic processes[51]. He set out a theory for what he called a Universal Turing Machine and led John Von Neumann to define an architecture for computers that is still used today. Although modern computers are more than twenty times faster, thousands of times more reliable, consume the power of a light bulb rather than that of a locomotive, occupy 1/30000 the volume and cost 1/10000 as much as those early models, the theory for their architecture was Turing's.[52]

The earliest electronic computers started to appear between the World Wars.

It was in 1938 that German engineer, Konrad Zuse, completed his Z1 computer. This was the first freely programmable computer which conformed to Turing's theory of a universal machine. Zuse had financed its development largely from his own money but, when the world returned to war, he got full funding from the Nazi government. As the conflict escalated, 'total war' ensued, the boundaries between civilian and military resources became less and less defined as all economic, industrial and scientific assets were thrown at winning an all out struggle.

---

51 Turing most famous paper was 'On Computable Numbers, with an application to the Entscheidungsproblem [Decision Problem]' which laid out the possible architecture of a 'Turing Machine' or computer.

52 These figures come from 'The Art and Science of Java" by Eric, S Roberts from Stanford University. It is available as part of a free online course in the fundamental principles of programming.

In Britain, Turing was moved to a full time position at Bletchley Park, the centre for deciphering coded enemy radio transmissions. Tasked with breaking the code generated by the German Enigma machine, he and the Bletchley team succeeded, against improbable odds. According to historians, their achievement was decisive in shortening the war certainly by two and possibly by as many as four years. Although Turing's genius was nurtured for the benefit of the war effort, he struggled in his personal life. He had to hide his homosexuality, illegal at the time, and was burdened with many characteristics which would probably be diagnosed now as Asperger's Syndrome, a mild form of autism. After the War he was charged with homosexuality and given a criminal conviction. By 1954, a broken man, he was apparently driven to kill himself with cyanide[53] although there were those who claimed his death was an accident. The half eaten apple[54] found by his bed was reminiscent of his favourite fairy tale, 'Snow White', but he had also set up an experiment in his spare room using potassium cyanide to dissolve gold and the cyanide fumes may have been fatal.

The great leaps forward in electronics and information processing were matched between the World Wars by advances in materials science. An early form of plastic

---

53 In September 2009 after an Internet campaign the then British Prime Minister Gordon Brown made a public apology on behalf of the British Government for the treatment of Turing, one of our greatest, but subsequently declined to give a full pardon.

54 The designer of the Apple logo and the Apple computer company have both denied that the half eaten apple was a homage to Turing. Recounting a conversation with Steve Jobs, Stephen Fry said Jobs' response was, 'It isn't true, but God, we wish it were'.

developed way back in 1905 by Belgian born New Yorker, Dr Baekeland was launched upon the world in a mouldable form as 'Bakelite' ten years later. The plentiful raw materials, coal tar or the by-products of the growing oil industry, made it cheap. It was perfect for mass production and it was an electrical insulator. Immediately adopted by the emerging electrical and radio industries, it was also used for everything from building materials to toys. Its usefulness was only limited by its brittleness.

The revolution in materials science continued in 1935 when chemist, Wallace Hume Carothers, synthesised two new materials, which were set to change everything from underwear to climbing gear. He had been working on the practical application of the theory German chemist Herman Staudinger had developed whilst working in neutral Switzerland[55] in the 1920s. His theory suggested the existence of long and complex chains of molecules called polymers and that these could be made by joining together lots of smaller chains in a repeating pattern. For a time no one believed this theory but it sparked research at several centres including at the American company DuPont where Carothers worked.

After much effort, Carothers and the DuPont team eventually managed to confirm Staudinger's theories when they discovered nylon alongside another new material. The team almost gave up, unable to see any practical application for the polymers they had succeeded in creating because of their low melting points but the long fibres of nylon, could be spun into thread, knitted, woven and braided. In the pre-polymer age, all threads, fabrics

---

55 A state that wishes to remain neutral to warring factions on its borders does so by treatise. Sweden declared its neutrality in 1814. Switzerland became the second internationally declared neutral state established by the Treaty of Paris in 1815.

and cordage were made from natural fibres; silk, wool and fibres from the husks, stems and seed heads of a multitude of plants. Marvellously multi-functional all of them but, from raw material to finished product, hugely labour intensive. It seemed that the new wonder material, nylon, could do all that these natural fibres could do and far more. It could be cheaply mass produced from a plentiful, easily available source. Unlike natural material, it did not rot and it was unappetising to vermin. It could be spun to any thickness to meet every purpose and it was extremely stretchy. The breaking strain of nylon thread far exceeded that of any natural fibre. Carothers and his team had found the Holy Grail of plastics.

Production was quickly industrialised and nylon stockings in particular, or just 'nylons' were sold in their millions. During the Second World War, production was switched to huge quantities of parachutes for the military. Nylon was also used to make ropes which could absorb shock loading in a way that was unique. At first the ropes were made by using nylon threads instead of hemp to copy the traditional hawser laid design; three thick strands made up of many individual twines twisted together. The vastly improved strength to weight ratio and elasticity were noted by climbers and that led to the construction of the first modern kernmantel rope by Edelweiss in 1953. This design used a woven sheath to protect the weight bearing twisted cords in the core of the rope from damage. These ropes were stronger, knotted more easily and were better at absorbing impact than hawser laid ropes. Woven nylon tape was also used to make slings and they in turn became the basis of the first climbing harnesses. So, without Staudinger's polymer theory and then Carothers' team at DuPont's research centre, climbers might still be climbing with hemp ropes tied round their waists. Years later Fred Hall from DMM, a leading climbing gear manufacturer, would name nylon in an interview as the most important material ever invented for rock climbing.

The inventor of the material which has become a mainstay of everyday modern life never saw its success. In common with many great minds, Carothers was plagued by depression. Winston Churchill graphically referred to his own depression as the 'black dog'[56]. Carothers often described himself as sitting 'sullenly at home'. In 1932, in a letter to a close friend about a speech he gave at an organic chemistry symposium, he wrote,

"It was pretty well received but the prospect of having to make it ruined the preceding weeks and it was necessary to resort to considerable amounts of alcohol to quiet my nerves for the occasion. … My nervousness, moroseness and vacillation get worse as time goes on, and the frequent resort to drinking doesn't bring about any permanent improvement. 1932 looks pretty black to me just now."

Despite being elected onto the prestigious National Academy of Science, life eventually proved too much for Wallace. His sister's death in 1937 seemed to tip him over the edge and even his psychiatrist felt that his subsequent suicide was a likely outcome. On April 28th that year Wallace took his life by drinking cyanide and lemon juice, knowing that the acidic solution would intensify and speed up the effect of the poison. Two years later, in 1939, his wonder material took the World Fair by storm.

Another technological step forward made during World War II enabled the 10th Mountain Division of the US Army to have aluminium karabiners. First used to lighten the equipment carried by those mountain troops, aluminium 'krabs' are now vital in any climber's rack. But

---

56 The 'Black Dog' Churchill often referred to was his battle with manic depression and he popularised the saying. But one of the earliest literary uses of the phrase in the modern context of mental woes, was by Samuel Johnson.

there were many initial problems with the use of aluminium in engineering. Three times lighter than steel, it had primarily been identified as an excellent material for building aeroplanes. However, whereas steel just required heating and then quenching in a cool fluid to toughen it, aluminium did not behave in the same way and it seemed to be impossible to harden it sufficiently. A German scientist, Alfred Wilm, had spent a long time attempting and failing to harden samples of an aluminium alloy when he interrupted his tests for a weekend sailing trip. He returned to a serendipitous discovery; being left for a few days, the metal had simply hardened over time. 'Age hardening' was the vital step that enabled many applications to be found for this new lightweight metal. Just before the World War II, Japanese engineers were using a particular alloy of aluminium, 7075, to build the airframe of the Zero fighter. That, coincidentally, is the most commonly used alloy for manufacturing karabiners today.

Although the Second World War marked a rapid scramble to develop new technologies to gain an advantage, many ultimately proved beneficial when peace finally came. But one scientific advance simultaneously handed the human race a new dawn of enlightenment and the means to destroy the planet. It was, of course, Albert Einstein who wrote to the then President Franklin D. Roosevelt only 3 months before War was declared. The letter warned of Germany's intentions to refine uranium-235 and create a new weapon that would release the massive and potentially destructive energy stored in every atom. Roosevelt's response was to set up the Manhattan Project[57] to match and surpass the Nazis' efforts to create

---

57 The Manhattan Project employed more than 100 000 people over its entire course, yet amazingly they believe that only a dozen people knew exactly what all the research and work was leading up to.

the Atom Bomb.

Leading scientist Julius Robert Oppenheimer was appointed and his team began the six years of work costing $2 billion it took to achieve the goal. Firstly, they dealt with the complexities of acquiring the unstable isotope of uranium needed for the bomb's destructive fission reaction; uranium-235. Twenty five tonnes of rare ore had to be processed to produce a single kilogram. A huge task, it proved to be a relatively minor problem because much of the six year period was spent developing the ground breaking science necessary to manage, contain and detonate the highly radioactive material. But eventually, all the hard work and dedication came to a dramatic conclusion when the new weapon was tested in the New Mexico desert at 5.30 am on July 16th 1945. The blinding flash made neighbouring communities believe the sun rose twice that day and there was a report of a blind girl 'seeing' the flash 120 miles away. Less than a month later the first nuclear warhead was constructed on the Pacific Island of Tinian and, on August 4th 1945, the B-29 bomber the Enola Gay flew it to Hiroshima and detonated the 13 kilotonne bomb over the city. Five days later, another B-29, Bockscar, finding its primary target obscured by cloud, dropped a second bomb over Nagasaki. Two hundred thousand people lost their lives in these two attacks and Japan capitulated. Victory in Europe was achieved on May 7th 1945 and three months later, the War in the Pacific too was ended.

Oppenheimer, like Nobel, was shocked at the destructive power of his invention and said that it reminded him of these words from the ancient Hindu scripture, Bhagavad Gita;,
"*Now, I am become Death, the destroyer of worlds*".

The lasting effect of knowing the destructive power of

the Atom Bomb continued long after World War II was over. The United States and her European allies entered into a Cold War with the United Soviet Socialist Republics which turned into a race to hold the most nuclear firepower as a deterrent. If one side had launched a weapon against the other, the automatic response would have been a counter attack with as many war heads as possible. The result has been described as mutually assured destruction or MAD. It took half a century for the threat of MAD to be brought under control. Over the same half century, power from the same source, the splitting apart of the atom, has been harnessed to provide electricity for millions.

After the end of the Second World War, companies equipped to mass produce   items for the war effort gradually turned to making the new technologies available to a different market. Economics dictated the need for huge numbers of consumers with enough income to buy the goods and enough leisure time to use them. Social attitudes in Britain had changed. People used their votes and their Trades Unions to demand better working conditions, health care and more free time. Ordinary people living in cities were determined to enjoy the countryside[58]. One estimate made in the 1920s of the number of people leaving Manchester by public and other transport every Sunday to go walking was 15 000. The mass trespass on Kinder Scout in 1932, established their claim to the right. The post-war Labour Government enacted legislation in 1949 to form National Parks and, ten

---

58 The Council for the Protection of Rural England made a film in 1936 that was shown in cinemas across the country. It encouraged the formation of National Parks for conservation and recreation. It can be seen here: http://www.youtube.com/watch?v=-fd2cCKISBA&feature=player_embedded#!

years later, ten such areas had been designated. As a result, when the development of mountaineering and rock climbing was resumed after World War II, many more people than ever before were ready to join in. This is the focus of the next chapter; when the 'working class hero' started to dominate the sport and cement the foundations of modern rock climbing.

5 THE EVOLUTION OF ROCK CLIMBING AND THE RISE OF THE WORKING CLASS HERO

The focus of this book so far has been on mountaineering where the climbers' objective is to sort out a summit. In the past, the routes they attempted up alpine peaks became harder and more sustained with a greater need to prepare and train for such challenges. As a result, more and more British mountaineers started to explore the rock climbing possibilities closer to home, before transferring those skills to the Alps and beyond.

The development of rock climbing has parallels with the evolution of mountaineering; first the easiest lines were climbed and then more difficult routes. Each generation set new challenges by launching from the test-pieces of the previous era into harder and bolder territory. The story of scaling rocks, is also the story of the participants who were no longer exclusively from the upper classes and who readily adopted new technology developed specifically for rock climbing.

An early venture into rock climbing territory was not by mountaineers but by a pair of botanists, the Reverends Peter Williams and William Bingley in 1798. Since they were not scaling a cliff simply for its own sake but on a foray to collect rare alpine plants, strictly speaking they were not engaged in rock climbing in the modern sense. But they did stumble upon Clogwyn Du'r Arddu on the flanks of Snowdon in their search for specimens and Bingley's description will sound familiar to any climber;

"I believe it was the prospect downwards that determined us to brave every difficulty. It happened fortunately that the steep section

immediately above us was the only one that presented any material danger. Mr. Williams, having a pair of strong shoes with nails in them, which would hold their footing better than mine, requested to make the first attempt, and after some difficulty he succeeded.... When he had fixed himself securely to a part of the rock, he took off his belt, and holding it firmly by one end, gave the other to me: I laid hold, and, with a little aid from the stones, fairly pulled myself up by it. After this we got on pretty well, and in about an hour and a quarter from the commencement of our labour, we found ourselves upon the brow of this dreadful precipice, and in possession of all the plants we expected to find."

Their climb took place on the highest point in England and Wales, which, like Everest, has two names. The traditional Welsh name, Yr Wyddfa, translates as 'tumulus' and is said to reference the legend of the defeat of the mythical giant Rhitta Gawr by King Arthur who erected a cairn over his body. Surprisingly, there is even less evidence for the originator of the English name, Snowdon. A leading contender is one of the earliest tourists, Thomas Pennant. He travelled extensively in Wales in the late 1700s writing several volumes on his journeys[59] and in one of these he recalls his visit and climb up 'Snowdon'. But evidence points to an earlier ascent which, together with some interesting coincidences, leads me to propose that the English name has different roots.

Although it is doubtful that a hill farmer or other resident in ancient times had not wandered up Snowdon before, it is Thomas Johnson, another botanist from

---

59 All his works have been scanned and displayed online by the National Library of Wales, and are available here, this link goes to the 6 Volume a part of which is entitled 'Journey To Snowdon'.

http://www.llgc.org.uk/digitalmirror/jts/JTS00006/18/unigol.html?lng=en

London, who is credited with the first ascent in 1639 and possibly with naming the mountain. Johnson lived and practised in a part of London called Snow Hill. The old English for Snow Hill is Snowdon. The reference to snow may also be a result of what is now generally known as the Little Ice Age recognised by NASA as being between 1550 and 1850 so there could have been snow on Snowdon for much longer periods when Thomas was visiting. Whatever the reasons, the sheer variety of alpine plants such as the rare Snowdon lily, the starry saxifrage and the plethora of other botanical wonders attracted the two Reverends and many other collectors of new species whose searches led them into steeper and steeper territory.

The first time rock climbing was the only objective of the excursion is generally acknowledged to be the ascent of Nape's Needle in the Lake District back in 1886. The first ascentionist, Walter Parry Haskett Smith, had already spent some time exploring the cliffs around Aber in Wales when on a university reading party six years earlier. Widely considered the 'Father of Rock Climbing' in the UK, Walter was a student at Oxford and a keen athlete. During one training session he managed to break the world long jump record, at the time 7.6m (25ft). Haskett Smith's ethos was to get rid of any climbing aids like ladders and instead focus on what is now called free climbing[60]. Inspired by the solo ascent of Napes Needle, O.G. Jones made an ascent of *Kern Knott's Crack* a climb graded VS[61] a year later in 1897.

---

60 Free climbing is often mistaken for soloing. Free climbing is the use only of natural hand and foot holds on the rock to gain height. The rope and the protection placed are there to save the climber in the event of a fall. Soloing is free climbing without a rope or gear for protection.

61 VS is the UK grade for a route deemed very severe, it is about equivalent to 5.8.

We can also be fairly sure that bouldering was also taking place by 1889 thanks to Haskett Smith who wrote this witty passage in his book which was published a few years later;

"A queerly-shaped rock on Great Napes, which in the middle of March, 1889 was gravely attacked by a large party comprising some five or six of the strongest climbers in England. It is a little difficult to find, especially in seasons when the grass is at all long."

Like most of his companions, Haskett Smith was educated at Eton before going onto study at Oxford. It would be several more years before rock climbing became a pastime for less privileged folk.

Climbing was not only occurring in the UK. There is considerable evidence to suggest that rock climbing began across the world almost simultaneously. The year after Napes Needle was ascended, a 17 year old school boy, Georg Winkler soloed the route *Die Vajolettürme* in the Dolomites. By the end of the 1800s there were around 500 active climbers on the Elbe Sandstone Mountains in Germany. At the same time, John Muir, a naturalist of Scottish descent, was journeying in America, his excursion around the Sierra Nevada Range in California being the most famous of his many trips in the area. In 1869 he made a solo ascent of Cathedral Dome in Tuolumne Meadows. On the rim of the Yosemite Valley for the first time and confronted by the 3000ft chasm, Muir noted that he could not *"help fearing that a little rock might split off"*.

He cautioned himself not to go back out there, but faced with such a breath-taking view, he was powerless to resist;

"One's body seems to go where it likes with a will over which we seem to have scarce control."

Other climbers in the US at the time are notable not for their free climbing but for their tenacity and ingenuity.

George Anderson bolted his way up Half Dome in 1875 and the fixed points are now the basis of today's 'easy walking route' where in summer two large cables are installed to aid walkers up this extreme domed peak. Similarly, the Devil's Tower, a beautiful thumb of rock in Wyoming which featured in the film *'Close Encounters of the Third Kind'*, was first ascended by William Rogers and Willard Ripley who pounded wooden chocks into cracks to fix a rope up to the plateau. It is no coincidence that they reached the top on Independence Day in 1893. A similar ascent was made a few years later in 1911 when John Otto created a veritable ladder up the Colorado State Monument, an impressive sandstone tower, again topping out on the 4th July.

On a trip across America in 2009, I repeated Otto's route. This 80 metre high isolated sandstone tower is situated in a canyon and getting to, and back from, the base requires a two hour hike down from the rim which has to be reversed later in the day. Otto's elaborate scaffolding is no longer there but I reflected in the oppressive heat of the canyon that simply getting the equipment to the base would have been a logistical epic let alone using it to climb the tower. How he must have felt chipping his way up this natural skyscraper, slowly edging upwards was something I asked myself as I followed in his footsteps. Today the scars of his work have made the route somewhat more accessible for climbers and, just when the going gets tough, there is nearly always a deep, positive three-finger drilled pocket made to anchor his scaffolding.

The final pitch goes easily at first up a whale back, breaching high against the desert sky. To help his progress (and mine) all he did was to cut steps. On either side are vertical drops that threatened to suck me into the void. At the end of this lonely staircase, the tower rears up like a tidal wave where the harder capping stone that has protected the softer sandstone below from erosion overhangs like a crashing wave. Even for a modern climber the 'out there' feeling of those final moves cannot compare with what Otto must have felt when he chipped the slot in which I placed the only protection, a single camming device. As I made my way over the final airy mantelshelf move, a small cheer came across from the tourists in the monument's Visitors' Centre. A kind welcome and a small reminder of the huge response Otto got nearly 100 years previously as he gained the summit and ran the Stars and Stripes up the flag pole on Independence Day in 1911.

At the beginning of the 20th Century, rock climbing for its own sake came into being. Oscar Eckenstein was teaching climbing techniques on boulders in Wales. Hans Fiechtl had redesigned the peg[62] used for protection, making it stronger by eliminating the thin ring and giving it an 'eye' instead, Otto Herzog started making climbing karabiners and a Chamonix Guide, Jean Esteril Charlet, perfected abseiling[63].

Shortly before the outbreak of World War I in 1914, alpinist Paul Preuss was the first to address the issue of ethics, in print at least, in his article in a German magazine. He coined the term 'artificial aid', advocated free climbing and criticised the increasing use of pegs to aid progress on ascents. In doing so, he sparked the great "Piton Dispute" and later wrote these six rules for ethically pure ascents;

---

62 The peg or piton is hammered into cracks in the rock and used to secure the rope (for protection) or to hold or stand on (aiding).

63 The term could have come from Austria or Germany since 'abseil' comes from the German abseilen, meaning "to down rope". Climbers also use 'rappel' from the French; "to return, withdraw or recall".

1. You should not be equal to the mountain climbs you undertake, you should be superior.

2. The degree of difficulty that a climber is able to overcome with security on the descent and also believes himself capable of with an easy conscience must represent the upper limit of what he climbs on the ascent.

3. The justification for the use of artificial aids consequently exists only in the event of an immediately threatening danger.

4. The piton is an emergency reserve and not the basis for a method of working.

5. The rope is permitted as a relief-bringing means but never as the one true means for making the ascent of the mountain possible.

6. The principle of security belongs to the highest principles. But not the frantic correction of one's own insecurity attained by means of artificial aids, rather that primary security which with every climber should be based in the correct estimation of his ability in relation to his desire.

Geoffrey Winthrop Young[64], one of the leading and most influential climbers of the day, supported Preuss in his ideas about ascents by fair means. This debate goes so deeply to the heart of climbing that it crops up perpetually as each generation of climbers struggles to redefine what ethical purity means to them given the technological advantages they have over previous generations. The views of Preuss were adopted by great climbers such as Walter

---

64 Geoffrey Winthrop Young was a leading climber in the early part of the 20th Century. He wrote a book on climbing the towers at Trinity College Cambridge, something which today would be grounds for expulsion. He also helped form the British Mountaineering Council. He was instrumental in the arrival of the German educationist Kurt Hahn in the UK, where he developed Outward Bound, one of the first uses of Outdoor Education in the world.

Bonatti[65], Reinhold Messner and Royal Robbins, all of whom avoided the use of bolts[66] at all costs.

This ethos of purity in ascent was intended to keep adventure to the fore in rock climbing. The routes the early climbers pioneered stand as a testament to what was possible with only a hemp rope, a few karabiners and some pegs. Astonishingly, many of these early routes are still graded HVS (or 5.9) and a precious few were even harder. One of my favourites of these early test-pieces is a climb made by Jack Longland in 1930 high up above the Idwal Slabs; *Javelin Blade* which is graded E1 (or 5.10) today. When Longland first climbed it, this was undoubtedly a much bolder proposition as modern equipment allows a small piece of protection to be placed reasonably close to the crux. He did not have that advantage and I suspect that if the route had to be climbed in the style of the first ascent today, it would warrant a grade of E2 or even the full rx grading in America. It led one climber from the Cambridge University Climbing Club to say it was,

"......... *an outstanding lead that stood as the most difficult piece of Welsh climbing for many years, though few were aware of it*".

Longlands never set out to raise the bar that day. That he was more of an accidental tourist was confirmed when he was subsequently asked about the ascent;

---

65 Italian Walter Bonatti made the fourth ascent of the North Face of the Grand Jorassess at age 18 and the first ascent of the Grand Capucin, a highly technical granite pillar, in 1951. He was surrounded by controversy after the first ascent of K2 in 1954 and the disaster in a terrible storm on Mont Blanc in 1962 but his reputation was later restored. He is considered to be one of the greatest mountaineers ever. 66 Bolts for protection are fixed in holes specially drilled in the rock in the UK in particular there is a strong ethic not to bolt routes in certain areas to maintain the adventurous spirit of traditional climbing.

"Quite frankly I'd lost my way. I'd come to the famous thread belay at the end of the first pitch of the normal route [Javelin Buttress VS], *and I didn't know that the route ought to go right. I was a pole vaulter, which I think gives you pretty strong fingers, and I remember the pull-out onto the actual blade of the javelin was very strenuous; though not dangerous – I had a belay about 40 feet below me."*

Now this seems a ridiculous understatement. To say that falling a possible 80ft onto a belay was not dangerous on hemp ropes is even something of a joke. Those strenuous moves often see off modern rock climbers with runners by their feet, wearing comfortable harnesses, decked out in sticky rubber rock shoes and belayed on nice stretchy climbing ropes.

Despite being criticised by many, the use of pegs as protection for free climbing rather than as direct aid was growing even though the need to carry a hammer and use two hands to place them limited their usefulness. However, four years before Longland's great climb, an early pioneer of Welsh crags, Fred Piggott, started experimenting with a new type of protection, the natural chock stone. Some accounts describe how he took a selection of small pebbles with him on what is now *Piggot's Climb* on Clogwyn Du'r Arddu and wedged these in tapering cracks with small loops of rope (slings) around them. However, a look at the 'First Ascents' pages at the back of the Climbers' Club guidebook to Cloggy[67], reveals a different story. Piggott's was the first name on the list of four climbers on the first ascent, the others were Morley Wood, L. Henshaw and J.F. Burton. Henshaw's version of events from an earlier attempt on the line says that Piggot may have successfully used natural chockstones but it was

---

67 The story is from Paul Williams, 1989 Climbers' Club Guides to Wales; Clogwyn Du'r Arddu (the Welsh name of the cliff that climbers have shortened to 'Cloggy').

not his idea;

"The plain fact is that Morley Wood was alone responsible for the idea of putting chockstones into the crack, the evidence being perfectly clear at this point. It may be said that the other members of the party were accessories after the fact; but Morley Wood was the one who conceived, organised and eventually put into practice his diabolical plan; and if some inserted pebbles did remain in, that can only be put down to Providence and not to any dexterity on his part."

Piggot and Morley Wood were at the cutting edge of climbing and were often criticised for employing modern techniques. It was Henshaw again who said of them,

"Nothing stops them and they stop at nothing,.... I shall not be surprised to see either of them turn up with the latest Sassolungo rock drill[68]*."*

What this team did however, was to change the game. Before this, only pegs, naturally occurring chock stones and spikes were available to protect the climber. By taking stones from the base of the crag, the ability to place protection quickly and in a greater variety of places developed.

Climbers soon realised that a rounder shape was better for this purpose so, in search of the perfect set of stones, they took to the stream beds. Once firmly wedged in place, the pebbles which could not be taken out provided 'in situ gear' for those doing later ascents but there seems not to have been any heated debate about it, not publicly at least. Since fiddling a sling around a chock stone whilst hanging on to tenuous holds must have been harder than placing a new one, most leaders would probably have preferred that they had all been removed. At the very least, these pebbles jammed in cracks far away from their original sources, will

---

68 A device developed by Laurent Grivel for placing expansion bolts for protection. Bolts have been avoided on natural rock in the UK giving the variety of traditional climbing (using gear selected and placed by the climber whilst leading) that is typical here.

give geologists of the future something to puzzle over.

The next step in the journey of climbing protection in Britain was made in the mid-fifties. But, since it was a logical development from natural chock stones and a re-use of existing technology, it seems less of an invention and more of a meme[69] or social contagion. Indisputably, the placing of chock stones naturally and almost spontaneously progressed to the widespread use of machine nuts[70] for protection. An account by veteran Peak District climber, Dave Gregory, recalls using machine nuts at that time on Cloggy. He and Jack Soper, a co-author of the definitive history of Cloggy, 'The Black Cliff', used to search the ballast of the Snowdon Mountain Railway where the tracks pass close to the crag. Their rather tongue in cheek superstition was that failure to find a nut on the approach would lead to failure on the day's climb.

In the UK, the limited size of the crags meant that climbers looked for new challenges by progressing free climbing through steeper terrain and the use of safer, more convenient protection devices allowed new ground to be broken. Further afield, where the most impressive cliffs are often very much bigger than those in the UK, a different form of climbing was developing; big wall aid climbing[71].

---

69 The evolutionary scientist, Richard Dawkins was looking for a word for the spread of an idea through society in much the same way that a genetic code spreads. He took the ancient Greek word mimeme and shortened it to so it was similar to gene. Meme is used for the rapid 'viral' spreading of knowledge and ideas through photos, videos and links through social media channels like Facebook.
70 The machine nut was the nut from a nut and bolt.
71 Aid climbing is the placing of gear to pull on instead of using hand and footholds to make progress.

Big wall climbing was first pioneered in Europe by a great Italian climber, Emilio Comici. The various techniques for big walling he developed include the use of multi-step ladders made from rope or slings for aid climbing and making solid belays with pegs or even bolts. The length and steepness of the routes he established also gave rise to the hanging bivouac. Comici conceived and developed his techniques on two famous walls in particular. His 1500m ascent of the North West Face of the Civetta with Enzo Benedetti in 1931 was a marathon of 26 pitches. The classic 1933 route on the North Face of the Cima Grande is regarded as one of the 'Great North Faces'. Half of the face is overhanging and it took him three days and two nights to complete the climb with brothers Angelo and Giuseppe Dimai. Comici said of climbing,

"On the mountains we feel the joy of life, the emotion of being good and the relief of forgetting earthly things: all this because we are closer to the sky".

Whilst the Dolomites saw success on longer and longer rock routes, on the outskirts of Paris in the forest of Fontainebleau, Pierre Allain was exploring the climbing possibilities of the myriad of boulders. At first these were used as a training ground for alpine climbing and long circuits made up of many problems were established. Amongst these, the notable *L'Angle Allain* was uncovered for the first time. This is a technical and, for most, baffling boulder problem which seems far harder than its V2 grade. In 1935, Allain had the vision to see the potential of the Fontainbleu boulders and perhaps because of his experience on the problems there, he saw the need for an innovation in footwear. Some rock climbers had switched from nailed boots to rubber-soled plimsolls[72] but Pierre Allain adapted these to bring the world its first specialised rock climbing boot. The name 'PAs' after their inventor quickly caught on and became the generic term for rock boots until the early 1980s.

At the time, the growing demand for rubber, especially for car tyres, was satisfied by increasing production of latex, the milky sap tapped from trees. But suppliers struggled to keep up and the price increased dramatically. A form of manmade rubber had been synthesized only a few years before but an effective way to manufacture it had not yet been found. Eventually, in April 1930, an American working for the DuPont company created a synthetic version in his laboratory. That American was none other than Wallace Carothers, the man who also discovered nylon. All of the many synthetic substitutes used today have been developed from his research although it was not until World War II that the potential of Carothers' material was realised and a multitude of uses were found for it.

In the devastation of the war so many promising climbers were amongst those lost. But it is Colin Kirkus[73] whose name still resonates around the cliffs of North Wales. His background was not public school and Oxbridge and he was not from the well off professional classes who dominated rock climbing in those days. This young insurance clerk was one of a growing number of

---

72 As now, plimsolls were canvas shoes with rubber soles. First used in tennis, they gave the name of an early route on the Idwal Slabs called Tennis Shoe.

73 A fuller life history can be found on the footless crow website. http://footlesscrow.blogspot.com/2011/05/colin-kirkus-gemini-rising.html

climbers from less privileged social backgrounds who were challenging the mountaineering establishment with sheer climbing talent and a willingness to push forward the boundaries of what was considered possible.

Born in 1910, Colin spent his holidays in North Wales and, at the age of 12, he was inspired by "British Mountain Climbs" by George Abrahams[74]. This became his bible and he soon took to climbing. There are epic tales of his cycling from his job in Liverpool to Snowdonia for action packed weekends and cycling home again, a round trip of 120 miles. In between, he often soloed many of the existing routes as well as establishing around 40 routes of his own, nearly all of which are still popular classics.

One of the first new routes he put up is on what is now a rather obscure crag in Cwm Lloer in the Carneddau. Climbing solo as he often did, Colin found himself committed in the final steep crack. Facing certain death if he were to fall, he managed to tie himself to a jammed block one handed with the rope he was trailing to elicit a rest. Undeterred and re-focused, he forged on only to have his rucsac become jammed just below the top. Yet again in a serious predicament, Colin finally freed himself from the rucsac and reached the end of the difficulties. It is one of the many routes he simply named *Kirkus' Route*. Another of the close calls Colin had whilst soloing happened when he was alone on a route called *Lazarus* above Idwal Slabs in the Ogwen Valley. Spread-eagled across the face over 500 ft above the ground, unable to retreat or ascend and with no one around to hear his calls, the situation was desperate. Somehow from his lofty perch he managed to find a footing and lasso a small distant spike. Houdini-like

---

74 Published in 1909 by Mills and Boon! The Abrahams brothers George and Ashley, from Keswick were climbers and photographers whose work recorded the evolution of climbing in the Lake District.

he had clutched success from the jaws of defeat once again.

With the coming of World War II, Colin would have been an ideal candidate to train people at the North Wales Mountain Warfare Unit. But he chose to follow his older brother into Bomber Command. Both brothers died, Colin being shot down in a raid over Bremen in 1942. Over his tragically short lifetime, Colin Kirkus made an indelible mark on the history of rock climbing in the UK. As well as the routes he established, his legacy includes his book for young climbers; "Let's Go Climbing". Commissioned by publishers Nelson and released in 1942, it   proved so popular and enduring in its appeal that it was reissued in 2004. Many climbers of subsequent generations cite it as a source of early inspiration and information. His direct, cheerful style is epitomised in this extract on how to get on to a narrow ledge using a move called a 'mantleshelf';

'…on an old fashioned mantlepiece. It is easy to raise yourself on to your hands, but surprisingly awkward to obtain a footing; a very delicate balance is needed. It is a good plan first to crowd the mantlepiece with all the ornaments that you most detest – those china dogs presented by Uncle Joe can take front place. A slight slip on your part – most unfortunate accident – and they are no more'.

Whilst Kirkus' explorations in North Wales were wide ranging, some of his contemporaries were focusing on the dark and forbidding crags on the North side of the Llanberis Pass. The gullies had all been climbed long before but very little impression had been made on the steep walls and cracks. Here, the most prolific pioneer in the decade before the Second World War was John Menlove Edwards. Almost forty new routes were put up in the Pass during these years, more than half of them by Menlove. With a somewhat reckless approach to loose rock, aided by great strength and exceptional boldness, he had a genius for spotting a line through improbable terrain which produced climbs still regarded as classic test pieces.

Greatly respected for his prowess on rock, Menlove felt he belonged in the climbing community where his homosexuality was largely ignored. A criminal offence in those unenlightened times and punishable by imprisonment, this could not be alluded to openly even when he fell in love with a 17 year old schoolboy called Wilfred Noyce who became a climbing partner. Menlove was prepared to be provocative however, naming one of his routes Sodom and causing great controversy. The Climbers' Club was compelled to ask him to change it and he dutifully called it Flying Buttress[75] instead. Although never completely accepted, at least Menlove had a place in this band of climbers until it was broken up when the War came and he found himself more vulnerable than ever.

The cliffs of the Pass and Cloggy were quieter during the War years of course but by no means deserted. New routes were established by climbers who found themselves on precious leave, in training or stationed in Llanberis. Others were non-combatants as was Menlove but he achieved less than a handful of first ascents during this period. True to his principles, he had declared himself a conscientious objector at the outset of the War. Public condemnation quickly followed in the newspaper in his hometown; the Manchester Guardian. A psychiatrist by profession, he moved away to work with traumatised children at the Great Ormond Street Hospital in London.

Isolation from his peers led Edwards to suffer from

---

75 If read as Flying But Stress, there is almost a joke on the CC in there as well?! Although to be fair the initial pitches do resemble the Gothic architectural feature.

bouts of depression, and his life[76] was shadowed by dark periods which were often reflected in the routes he climbed. Eventually, as his mental condition worsened, Menlove's feats became more and more outrageous. He was known to swim the white water of the Lin of Dee and row single handed from the Isle of Man to Cumbria as well as turning to more hideously loose and vegetated climbs around North Wales. He was driving home from there in 1957 when he knocked down and killed a young boy. It was the beginning of the end. Increasingly paranoid and with growing feelings of worthlessness and hopelessness, Menlove eventually took his own life by taking potassium cyanide. His bequest to subsequent generations of rock climbers is invaluable.

During the closing stages of the War, the British electorate unceremoniously dumped their government and voted for a National Health Service, Welfare Reform and secondary education for all to the age of fifteen. Clearly there was a widespread desire for change and a general feeling that it was about time the 'land fit for heroes' promised after World War I should be delivered. Ordinary working people took the opportunity to vote in a government whose members had backgrounds similar to their own. Commerce also supported the reforms. Manufacturers adapting wartime technologies and creating peacetime markets needed skilled and educated workers with sufficient leisure time[77] to use the products and high enough wages to buy them.

---

76 Jim Perrin's book Menlove: The Life of John Menlove Edwards, gives a compelling and full account of his life.

77 The 2 day 'weekend' was established in the US in 1940. Credit goes to their Labor Movement. But as early as 1926 it was standard in the car factories of the far sighted Henry Ford who recognised that workers with no leisure time to use cars would not buy them.

The change in attitudes accelerated the growth in the number of people from all social backgrounds who wanted to try rock climbing. The hold of the climbing establishment, originally almost entirely from the leisured upper and professional classes, was still very much in evidence but it had been continuously eroded over the decades since the 1900s. This was inevitable. The crags and mountains did not discriminate on the grounds of social class and the many people who were now prepared to just turn up and 'have a go' were oblivious to the edicts of the great and good of the Alpine Club and the Climbers' Club.

The Peak District[78] in particular was accessible by public transport or bike from Manchester and Sheffield and the gritstone edges became busier as new enthusiasts joined those who had begun climbing before the War or during their time in the services. Many were inspired and informed by the proliferation of guidebooks, instructional texts, maps and climbing literature to be found in public libraries. The routes put up by successive generations of pioneers in the Lakes and North Wales tested and honed the skills of those able to go further afield, often travelling by motorbike and camping or 'bivvying' to save money.

Basic but adequate outdoor gear was sold in War (later Military) Surplus shops. Clothing, waterproofs, tents, 'snap links' as karabiners were called and boots, both nailed and Vibram[79] soled, were all relatively cheaply available. These climbers were not well equipped especially by modern standards but the occasionally not entirely legal ways they had to eke out their limited funds are legendary. It was

---

78 In 1951 the Peak District became the first National Park in UK.

79 Patented in 1937 by Italian mountaineer Vitale Bramani with financial support from Pirelli tyres after the deaths of six of his friends in climbing accidents were blamed on inadequate footwear.

very common to use washing lines, usually stolen and in various states of disrepair, instead of expensive hawser laid ropes. In those days before there were harnesses it was usual just to tie the end around the waist. Better, but this needed more rope, was to wind some turns of a separate length around the waist with the ends tied together like a wide belt called a 'waistline'. With the climbing rope tied round the 'belt', it would not tighten in the event of a fall and the cheese wire effect was lessened. With excruciating consequences either way, no wonder the guiding mantra of 'the leader must not fall' was still as popular as ever.

Climbers from the same workplaces or areas often grouped together in informal clubs to swap news, plan trips and arrange to share transport and gear. One such was the Rock and Ice Club; a dozen or so members, most with some climbing experience who all lived on the edge of Manchester. Fired by friendly competition but mostly by mutual encouragement, they were largely unrestrained by external codes of ethics and the disapproval of anyone but their mates. With an average weekly wage of about £7 they were practically teetotal because beer ate into precious climbing funds. Weekends were short, starting at midday Saturday for most of them, but they managed as many trips to crags away from home as possible. They excelled at the hard technical climbing demanded by their local gritstone, frequently put up new routes and their reputation grew.

The collective talent of the Rock and Ice Club was formidable but the group all acknowledged that their most gifted member was Joe Brown. Manchester born and bred, Joe was the seventh child in his family and he became an apprentice plumber on leaving school. He had been exploring the Peak District since he was 12 and had been inspired by Colin Kirkus' book for youngsters. He later spent 3 years in the Valkyrie Club until it disbanded and then he climbed with the bunch of mates who became the Rock and Ice and his future rock stardom was assured.

Joe Brown was one of two huge talents who led the UK climbing scene in the 50s and 60s. The other was Don Whillans. Together and separately they took climbing to a whole new level. Coming from nearby Salford and, coincidentally, also an apprentice plumber, Don was already known as a climber in the area. Although each certainly knew of the other's reputation, surprisingly, the pair did not meet until 1951.

Joe was at The Roaches that day, a crag just outside Leek in Staffordshire. An old hand here, where the Valkyrie Club had pioneered the hand jam technique on the wide gritstone cracks that split the cliff, Joe had already put up 'Saul's Crack' five years before. At HVS[80] that had marked a completely new standard of achievement. Today he was attempting another new route but his partner was struggling vainly to follow the first pitch. Through the crowd that had gathered strolled Don whose offer to relieve the poor second was promptly accepted. Tying on, he cruised the awkward crack and, invited to lead through by Joe, he made quick work of the rest of the widening cleft and the final bulge. 'Matinee', so called because of the enthralled audience who had watched the performance, was completed and given a grade of HVS. As a route, it has become a 3 star classic but it was far more significant as the first new route of one of the most influential partnerships in the history of British climbing.

Don joined the Rock and Ice and between 1951 and

---

80 Hard Very Severe, is a British grade from the early system of route grading as Easy, Moderate and Difficult, which was eventually extended by the severe grade. These were then extended again with the addition of Hard, Very and Extremely.

1955, the pair picked off all the obvious major cracks at the Roaches to produce a whole series of classics. All have what is still recognisably the Brown-Whillans trademark; uncompromisingly steep, fiercely strenuous lines which only succumb to a bold and determined approach. Others were willing to try steep, even vertical terrain, even walls that lean back slightly, but Whillans was an early pioneer of climbing through overhangs and roofs. In January 1954 he put up 'The Sloth' with Joe. It was probably the first roof to be free climbed. Rock climbing in Britain had never seen anything quite like it.

Over the same period, Joe and Don were also putting up routes in their unmistakable style on crags further afield especially in North Wales. All the members of the Rock and Ice were exceptionally talented and during the fifties the club virtually monopolised the long, challenging new routes on the forbidding mountain cliff, Clogwyn Du'r Arddu. Often climbing together but sometimes with others, Joe and Don put up more than twenty of them. These quotes from the Anthology of First Ascents section of Nick Dixon's 2004 Climbers' Club guide to Cloggy gives their achievement some perspective;

Geoffrey Sutton on Joe Brown; *"Other climbers who had hitherto been considered at the very top of the ladder tried to repeat his climbs (often in good conditions when the first ascent had been done in bad) and failed........"*

Nick Dixon on a route called Taurus; *"A typical Whillans shocker that has stood the test of time. It is thought by many to be worth E4, in which case it would be one of the earliest climbs of that grade."*

Their impact on the crags of the Llanberis Pass was equally momentous. After repeating the established routes of an earlier pioneer, Menlove Edwards, the Rock and Ice

Club were prolific in putting up their own, typically choosing lines previously thought to be impossible. Joe was foremost in this effort of course and his routes have been described as a 'major discoveries' and 'great milestones in Welsh climbing'.

Two of his most remarkable routes were supposedly named after destinations of Manchester buses and they are suitably macabre; *Cemetery Gates* and *Cenotaph Corner*. Both are on the imposing Dinas Cromlech which is formed by two vertical football pitches of rock joined at right angles like an open book for giants on whose pages are written some of the greatest achievements of subsequent generations of climbers. *Cemetery Gates* follows the right arête and Brown made the first ascent with Whillans soon after they met. Worn by frequent traffic now, it was then covered in friable little flakes and that day it also rained. *Cenotaph Corner* takes the spine of the book, one of the most aesthetically compelling lines in the world and was finally established by Brown with Doug Belshaw in 1952.

The first attempt on *The Corner* provides an appropriately epic tale. As Joe approached the top of the route, he stopped to place a peg before the crux. Fighting the mental tension and growing pump, he finally seated the peg in place. Reaching down for the rope between his legs, he struggled to pull up any slack. Instinctively he shouted "Slack!" and the peg hammer, held between his clenched teeth, plummeted down the corner. As it fell Joe wondered whether to shout a warning and have his belayer hit in the face as he looked up or do nothing and have it hit him on the top of the head. He ran out of time. The second was knocked unconscious and they were forced to retreat from the route that day. The first ascent was eventually made in 1952, using natural chockstones, pegs and machine nuts for protection.

During the first half of the 50s, the members of the new breed of rock climbers were regularly visiting the Alps to try their hand on long, hard mountain routes. Travelling cheaply and usually camping they were putting up new routes very much of the same character as their trademark routes on the crags at home; steep and hard. Typical of this genre was Brown and Whillans' new route on the West Face of l'Aiguille de Blaitière. Called the "British Route", the hardest pitch was long considered to be the awkward offwidth "Fissure Brown". A bold prospect, Joe and Don found it could be protected with a large chock stone which they removed afterwards. Unaware of this technique, the French pair making the second ascent, Paragot and Bérardini, concluded that the Brits were 'mutants'. Others repeating the route drove large wooden wedges into the crack as protection. These have long since gone but most modern leaders resort to huge size 4 camming devices.

Although Brown, Whillans and the groups of climbers from similar working backgrounds were rapidly making names for themselves at home and abroad, none as yet had experience of the Greater Ranges although it was widely considered only to be a matter of time, such were their reputations. This was a wholly correct assumption[81] as it turned out before the decade was over. But it was coincidental that, just as Joe and Don were loading their motorbikes with gear for an early trip to the Alps in the summer of 1953, the British Everest Expedition was leaving for the attempt which ultimately and famously achieved long awaited success.

The expedition was funded and the team was selected

---

81 In 1955 Brown was invited on the expedition which made the first ascent of Kanchenjunga and Whillans was on a successful expedition to Annapurna two years later.

by a joint committee from the Alpine Club and the Royal Geographical Society. Unsurprisingly, competition for places on the team had been intense and successful applicants were amongst the best known British mountaineers with experience of the Himalaya. Almost all were required to take on a second role and were appointed as doctors, physiologists, photographers and film makers amongst other jobs. The leader was John Hunt and this was a surprise because all the reconnaissance expeditions since the 30s had been led by Eric Shipton whose exploration in 1951 had found the access route from the south and sketched out the approach through the Khumbu icefall. Shattered by being dropped from the leadership for the 1953 bid, Shipton must have had some satisfaction that his legacy extended to the inclusion of two other members of the team; Edmund Hilary and Tensing Norgay.

Shipton tells the story in his autobiography *'That Untravelled World'* of how Hilary and his climbing partner George Lowe came to be on his 1951 reconnaissance expedition. Two days before it departed, a letter arrived from the President of the New Zealand Alpine Club asking if they could join it. Initially dubious because of lack of funds, Shipton relented when he remembered how the unstuffy cheerfulness of a Kiwi on a previous trip had been an asset. The fact that Hilary and Lowe were already conveniently located in the Garhwal Himalaya having knocked off six first ascents may or may not have been a factor in his decision. He also recounts

"… another prophetic incident. From a hundred applicants, we chose fifteen Sherpas to accompany the expedition from Darjeeling…there was one Tibetan lad of nineteen, a newcomer, chosen largely because of his attractive grin. His name was Tensing Norkay."

Tensing Norgay was also a talented climbing sherpa who went on to reach a high point of around 8000m with the Swiss Everest expedition the following year! Whimsical or not, Shipton's judgement resulted in Hilary[82] and Tensing being given the opportunity to gain experience of the approach which must have made their selection for John Hunt's ultimately successful 1953 expedition largely a foregone conclusion.

The success of the Everest Expedition raised the profile of mountaineering worldwide. It was one of the major events of the decade, with the news breaking just days before Queen Elizabeth II's Coronation. Snowdonia had also recently been declared a National Park for all to enjoy. Greater numbers of people than ever before responded by showing an interest in the outdoors, sparked at least in part by a "Victory" tour of the UK which included Tensing Norgay. Visiting the Pen y Gwryd Hotel, close to Snowdon, to see where the British members of the team had trained he gazed up at the mountain for a while. Companions thought he was comparing its size to that of Everest and trying to frame a tactful comment. But, accustomed only to the scale of peaks at home, Tensing asked how many days the climb would take.

The increase in the number of people participating in mountaineering and rock climbing was boosted by the popularity of the firmly established Outward Bound movement and the growing number of climbers finding employment as instructors to novices. Inevitably innovation in equipment design followed. Nylon ropes made to a hawser laid design and the use of a stiff canvas belt instead of the rope 'waist line' were by now commonplace.

The drawbacks of the chock stones and machine nuts

---

82 Becoming close a friend of Tensing, Hilary set up a charity, the Himalayan Trust. Begun in 1960, its work for sherpa families still continues.

threaded on rope that had served climbers well for so long were being closely examined in some quarters. The sense that climbing and mountaineering should be as safe as possible for growing numbers of new participants and the desire of the most talented to attempt harder and harder routes created a necessity. This was about to be satisfied by those with design ideas and those with technical knowledge of the available materials. Two questions needed to be asked; 'What is needed?' and 'What is possible?'[83]

In 1961, a keen climber and teacher of engineering technology from Sheffield, John Brailsford[84], created the first specifically designed metal chock. Named after the acorn it resembled, this was a tapered cylinder threaded on a nylon sling with a drilled out machine nut. Effectively, a climber slotting protection into a crack now had a choice of two sizes and shapes available on one sling. The Acorns were first sold in the Roger Turner Mountain Shop in Nottingham. But Brailsford went on to design the first chock whose shape would be familiar to any climber who uses leader placed protection today. John had these made from his balsa wood prototypes in cast LM6 aluminium which was chosen for its corrosion resistance, durability and impact strength. Aware of research into rope breaking strain, he adjusted the way it was threaded through this wedge shaped piece of metal to maximise its strength and

---

83 Path-dependent Foundation of Global Design-driven Outdoor Trade in the Northwest of England, International Journal of Design, M.B. Rose, T. Love & M Parsons, 2007.

http://www.ijdesign.org/ojs/index.php/IJDesign/article/view/160/79

84 The name Brailsford will sound familiar: John's son Dave oversaw the success of British cyclists at the Olympics in Beijing and London and in the 2012 Tour de France. He is currently British Cycling's Head of Performance.

the result was the MOAC. A friend of Brailsford had suggested the name 'Johnny' after the slang term for another form of protection, the condom. But Ellis Brigham, who owned a chain of shops and an import business called Mountain Activities, had funded the first die cast production run. He chose to use the first two letters of each word of the name of his business to give the world the MOAC.

Just like generations of climbers before (and since) them, contemporary climbers endlessly debated the ethics they applied and the style in which routes were done. Respect for the style of the first ascent, a desire not to damage the rock and not to 'steal' routes from future generations by leaving 'in situ' permanently fixed protection were all issues which caused concern. When the removable chock became widely available, the peg became a less glorifying means with which to 'murder the impossible'[85]. It became hugely popular for more pragmatic reasons too. Easily carried (unlike chock stones), readily available to everyone (unlike drilled out machine nuts) and designed to fit almost every crack (unlike anything else), MOACs and their like revolutionised the safety and confidence with which leaders could tackle routes.

Other shapes and designs quickly followed, the modern generic terms for these being 'nuts' or 'rocks'[86]. Most had

---

85 This turn of phrase came from a Reinhold Messner article

http://upwardtrail.multiply.com/journal/item/1/The_Murder_of_the_Im possible

86 There are two good sites worth visiting, one is needles sports nuts story and the other Stephane Pennequin Nuts Museum.

http://needlesports.com/NeedleSports/nutsmuseum/nutsstory.htm

http://www.mtntools.com/NutsMuseum/01.html

the universally useful wedge shape but one type also had another important innovation; being threaded on steel wire. The designer, Charles Curtis, called these 'Little Mesters' after the craftsmen who made cutlery and silverware in the 19th and early 20th centuries in Sheffield. He was there working in the university's geology department when he met student members of the caving club who were making their own wire ladders. Curtis got a sample of the wire, knotted it and poured molten aluminium onto it to make a prototype of his new chock. He gave it to climbers Pete Crew and Jack Soper to try out on their attempt to make a second ascent of the Tremadog classic *Vector*[87]. Jack was leading on the final awkward and heart stopping layback crack. This is still hard today but back then it was full of mud. Slipping off in the glop, Jack's weight came onto the new chock and it fell apart. A spectacular fall was the immediate result followed shortly afterwards by the realisation that the heat of the molten aluminium had radically altered the properties of the steel wire. In the next version, the wire was inserted into a pre-cast block.

The rapid move to the use of removable protection in the UK was slow to cross the Atlantic where climbers were preoccupied with some big walls which eclipsed even those of the Dolomites. The Yosemite Valley is a spectacular trench carved by glaciers eons ago where the sky is enclosed by some of the longest and most consistently steep rock faces in the world. These walls had been in the sights of climbers for a while but the biggest had rebuffed all comers until the late fifties.

One of the very first conservationists, the Scot John Muir again, persuaded the American government to declare Yosemite a National Park in 1890. On an early visit he said that,

---

87 Another of Joe Brown's legacies.

"No temple made with hands can compare with Yosemite.....the grandest of all special temples of Nature."

The photographer Ansel Adams agreed with that sentiment. Prints of his classic views are still among the best images of Yosemite and he has inspired generations of adventurers, tourists, photographers and climbers and given people the world over a sense of the place. But nothing prepares you for seeing it with your own eyes. There are three ways into the Valley and each has its moment of dramatic revelation when for the first time you see the immense size of El Capitan. On my first visit I pressed my face against a bus window, trying unsuccessfully to get the whole cliff into view; a vertical mile of rock, over two miles wide and steeped in history. I was hit square in the face by the shock and awe of nature and the Valley's stunning beauty. The early big wall pioneers here had no doubt that 'El Cap' was the jewel in the crown but its sheer scale and apparently featureless rock kept climbers at bay.

It was going to take a maverick or a madman or someone who was both to climb the immense wall. That man was Warren Harding, whose assault on the biggest cliff in the Valley, if not the world, began in 1957. His audacious plan had an element of revenge. Harding had previously attempted the North West face of another of Yosemite's iconic cliffs, Half Dome. He had been unsuccessful but when he returned for another go he found that he was too late. His rival, Royal Robbins had beaten him to the ascent by a matter of days. Down beat and wondering what to do, he and partners Mark Powell and Bill 'Dolt' Feuerer hatched an outrageous plan;

"The solution was simple; any climb less than Half Dome was beneath us; only a great climb would do."[88]

---

88 Warren Harding quoted in "Big Wall Climbing" by Doug Scott – Oxford Press 1976.

The route they chose, called 'The Nose' on El Cap, is still a formidable route even today. Then it was regarded as virtually impossible. Harding was determined to succeed so his tactics were perhaps understandable but they were compared unfavourably with Robbins'. On their ascent of Half Dome, Robbins and his team had climbed the North West Face in 'alpine style'; from ground to the top in one continuous push, removing gear as they went. In contrast, Harding turned the ascent of the Nose into a long drawn out siege. Permanent protection and ropes were fixed, camps were established and the team regularly descended to collect more gear. The whole enterprise resembled an attempt on a Himalayan peak and arguably some bamboo grows quicker than their average daily height gain.

The first problem encountered by Harding and his team was a wide uninterrupted crack carved into the granite face for over 700 feet. Unable to find a wide enough peg, they descended and team member Frank Tarver went away to cut the legs off several wood burning stoves he found in a refuse dump. Using these as extra wide pegs, the team protected the revered crack by hammering them into it and gave it the name it has today, the *Stove Legs Crack*.

Before long, news of Harding's endeavours spread throughout the US. His team became a tourist attraction and hoards of onlookers regularly filled the meadow below the wall. Park authorities asked for a halt until after the holidays when the crowds would all go home but Harding's team could not stay that long and he was left alone. By recruiting any unsuspecting climbers he could find to help complete his madcap scheme, he topped out on November 12th 1958 after an epic fifteen hours drilling 28 expansion bolts into the final head wall pitch. The 18 month siege that saw 45 days of climbing and 125 bolts employed to realise Harding's dream of climbing The Nose on El Cap was finally over.

Shortly afterwards, Royal Robbins, Tom Frost, Chuck Pratt and Joe Fitschen repeated the route. Climbing it in alpine style, they took only seven days. The same team minus Joe went on to make the first ascent of Salathe Wall in the same way. These ascents gave ammunition to Harding's critics who maintained he had forced his route by 'stealing the impossible'. Perhaps unsurprisingly, it was Royal Robbins who returned from a trip to the UK some years later with a set of chocks obtained from Joe Brown's climbing shop in North Wales. These were the first seen in the US. Using them to make hard new routes without scarring the rock or leaving permanently fixed gear, Robbins led the move in American climbing to define a purer form of ascent, where style is everything.

The history of all human achievement is mostly a fairly unexciting story of the steady evolution and growth of knowledge and skills. But every now and then there is a huge leap forward when one of a few with exceptional talent takes on a challenge thought to be impossible by ordinary mortals and succeeds. Then the world is changed for everyone. The 'impossible' is now further away waiting for another genius to make another breakthrough. In the meantime, the rest of us get on with trying what we used to think was impossible since it has been shown to be just extremely difficult. In doing so, we drive the general level of achievement up a few notches.

The psychological barrier presented by a definition of what is 'possible' is very real until it is breached. No longer prevented by the belief that what they are trying is 'impossible', others can then follow and the barrier breaks down. Sometimes this happens remarkably quickly, sometimes it takes a generation or more, but it does break down. Of course, it is then replaced as the most talented reach what seems to be close to a new limit of what can possibly be achieved. A stark example of such a psychological barrier is what used to be the Holy Grail for middle distance runners, the four minute mile. Once Roger Bannister had broken through that ceiling in 1954, only two months later, the Australian John Landy also ran a mile in less than four minutes. It was not long before the 'sub-four' mile was almost ordinary.

In rock climbing, the psychological barriers are less clear cut. Since Napes Needle was first climbed and rock climbing became a pastime in its own right, what has been considered 'impossible' has always been very subjective. In the early days of the sport, climbers used the word 'impossible' with no inhibitions. Gully lines were climbed first and the walls in between were often deemed impossible. Then along came Colin Kirkus. The steep crags of the Llanberis Pass were left alone until Menlove Edwards put up route after route. The huge buttresses of Cloggy were very lonely places until the Rock and Ice Club arrived. There are many other examples from the Lakes to the gritstone edges, from the Dolomites to Yosemite. Some routes seemed impossible because no one had yet developed a way of climbing them that worked. Then the ideal technique evolved for   awkward offwidth cracks, roofs and other insuperable problems and they became fair game for all. Many crags and lines were thought to be impossible because they could not be climbed safely even by the very bold. Then climbers from successive eras used chock stones, or pegs, or machine nuts or specifically made gear to protect them.

Every break through opened up new possibilities; yesterdays impossible became today's cutting edge and finally tomorrow's trade route. So climbers have become much more circumspect about using the word 'impossible'.

The truth is any line, any route can be climbed if the climber is prepared to "murder the impossible" so the ethics applied provide the key. Essentially, good style involves using gear only where necessary to ensure safety while preserving the inherent difficulty of the climb. With this principle firmly established, systems for grading the difficulty of climbs have often had to be refined as the limits of possibility are relentlessly pushed ever higher and as better climbing equipment was developed.

In the fifties, the boundaries of possibility were being redrawn in every field of human endeavour. But the beginning of the next decade was about to be marked in a truly astonishing way. A huge leap of scientific imagination and faith in technology had been made and preparations were under way for the first attempt to send a human beyond the boundaries imposed by the planet. This possibility had become a probability within a single generation. If it became a reality others would surely follow.

6 THE SWINGING SIXTIES AND THE SPACE RACE

As a child growing up in the seventies, the sixties were part of the recent past and for me they are immediately associated with psychedelic drugs, the peace movement and sexual freedom. But delve deeper and the sixties represent a dramatic turning point for western society. A current of change swept the world then like a tsunami which left behind the foundations of the freedoms we have come to take for granted; universal equal rights, a global environmental movement and the expectation that technology could make anything possible.

Technological advancement was as key to this momentous decade as social change. The sixties, in the sense of the movement, spanned from 1963 to 1974 and saw many great achievements including the development of fundamental technologies that drive today's digital society.

The greatest of those achievements was undoubtedly the technology which enabled men to walk on the moon. The 'Space Race' made the limits of what was possible seem to be as infinite as space itself and sparked the belief that humans could achieve anything if they were to put their minds to it. Crucially, it had a direct bearing on the speed with which news could be communicated. Previously, news could be passed within minutes by radio or telephone across the world, but because of the Space Race news could be broadcast via television within a fraction of a second of an event happening. Live television broadcasts became possible and the world immediately seemed smaller. Only slightly less earth-shattering was the massive effect of early live broadcasts on the public's perception of climbing but more of that later.

One essential component of space travel was developed during the Second World War. The Treaty of Versailles, agreed at the end of the First World War banned research into and use of long range super cannons. It was in a bid to circumvent the treaty that the Germans recruited several leading engineers to figure out how to use rocket propelled missiles to launch longer range attacks. They included a young engineering prodigy called Wernher Von Braun. An aristocrat by birth, he had been inspired by Herman Oberth's book '*By Rocket into Interplanetary Space*' which drew on the writings of Jules Verne. Von Braun would later say to the renowned explorer Auguste Piccard[89] "*I plan on travelling to the moon at some point.*" He did not do so but his ambitions were at least partly realised many years later.

The team developed the A-4 rocket which, during production tests, became the first manmade object to enter space. But later, as the V2 missile, it caused devastation from 1944 to the end of the war when more than 3000 were targeted on London. Each carried a 1000kg warhead and travelled at 4000 kph. Defence against them was virtually impossible and they killed an estimated 7000 people. So it was little wonder that, as war in Europe came to an end, Russia, America and the United Kingdom all scrambled to recruit the German rocket engineers to further their weapons programmes. Von Braun[90] ended up in America where he helped develop a military missile

---

89 Auguste Piccard was a Swiss physicist, inventor and explorer who managed to ascend to 23km in his hot air balloon, he was also father of Jacques Piccard, who we shall meet later in this chapter.

90 Von Braun never travelled to the moon, but as first director of the NASA Marshall Space Centre he helped the Apollo program to succeed.

called the Redstone.

By 1955 the communist states of the Soviet Union and the United States and her allies were firmly entrenched in the Cold War. Both sides were preoccupied with a terrifying proliferation of weaponry but space exploration continued with plans to launch 'small earth circling satellites'. Three years later, only four days separated the announcements from both sides that their respective projects were near completion. The Russians beat the Americans by reducing the size of their satellite, Sputnik 1, which went into orbit on 4th October 1957 and stayed there for three months collecting and transmitting data by radio. The American launch had been held back. To avoid accusations of warmongering, the President ordered that the military Redstone rocket be redesigned as a civilian version called Juno before delivering their Explorer 1 satellite into orbit. Successfully launched some seven months later, it produced an immediate result by confirming the theoretically predicted existence of a belt of radiation around the earth. But the USSR had been first and Eisenhower was never forgiven by the American electorate.

The Soviet Union followed up on their initial success by being the first of the two super powers to launch a man into space and see his safe return[91]. In 1961 Yuri Gagarin

---

91 The Russians held the International Federation of Aeronautics (IFA) record for this feat but until 1978 hid from the world that their pilot had not landed the spacecraft but had ejected at 7000 metres and landed by parachute. This broke IFA rules that stipulated that pilot and aircraft must return safely to earth together. Unaccountably, only the IFA seemed to care. The Russians certainly did not.

became the first cosmonaut[92]. The pressure of the US being behind in the propaganda war of technological one-upmanship was felt by President John F. Kennedy. Within one week he asked the US space programme specifically to see if they could find an opportunity to catch up with or overtake the Russians. A few weeks later Vice-President Lyndon B. Johnson recommended a piloted moon landing. Less than a month after that, JFK backed the proposed Apollo programme and made a special address to Congress in May 1961 which laid out his aims for a space programme to the American people;

"First, I believe that this nation should commit itself to achieving the goal, before this decade is out, of landing a man on the moon and returning him safely to the earth. No single space project in this period will be more impressive to mankind, or more important for the long-range exploration of space; and none will be so difficult or expensive to accomplish. We propose to accelerate the development of the appropriate lunar space craft. We propose to develop alternate liquid and solid fuel boosters, much larger than any now being developed, until certain which is superior. We propose additional funds for other engine development and for unmanned explorations--explorations which are particularly important for one purpose which this nation will never overlook: the survival of the man who first makes this daring flight. But in a very real sense, it will not be one man going to the moon--if we make this judgment affirmatively, it will be an entire nation. For all of us must work to put him there."

In the same speech he also made proposals for developing and launching satellites for global communication and world-wide weather observations. Essentially, JFK was launching the USA's all out attempt to win the space race by defining a new set of goals.

By September 1963, JFK must have realised that his dream was going to be harder and more expensive than he thought and, in a speech to the United Nations, he

92 Cosmonaut roughly translates to 'sailor of the universe'.

proposed that the US join forces with the Russians to achieve the goal of putting a man on the moon. The Russian premiere Nikita Khrushchev almost took him up on the idea, as the two leaders had developed a respectful rapport. Within two months the possible collaboration was off; Kennedy had been assassinated. Each of the superpowers went on to follow its own mission and a surge of technological developments resulted.

Computers to do the thousands of necessary calculations very rapidly and with total accuracy were clearly essential but the problem was that then they were huge, very temperamental and were only understood by the boffins who built them. The need for the space programme to have smaller, lighter but still more powerful computers led to many advances. They had to be capable of being programmed by engineers, designers[93] and lots of experts other than mathematical geniuses so the Beginners' All-purpose Symbolic Instructional Code, or the BASIC programming language was produced in 1963. The moon landings were achieved using a computer with fewer computing capabilities than one of the first handheld mobile phones that only made calls and sent text messages. But from that point on, computers revolutionised how data are processed and machines are operated with the only limitation being the creativity of those finding applications for them.

One of the many almost unknown talents whose work is responsible for the widespread use of computers we take for granted is Jack Kilby. After attending university, he

---

[93] Computers have been central to the equipment design process and crucially important in engineering the smaller, lighter karabiners we use today.

started work at Texas Instruments[94] where, being new to the company, Jack did not get a summer vacation. Instead, he turned his mind to a problem with computer circuits that was described as the 'tyranny of numbers'. In outline, the problem was that a more powerful computer required more components which all had to be connected by hand soldered wires to thousands of other components. The amount of space needed and the sheer complexity of the wiring would be a limiting factor in the power of a computer.

Kilby began by exploring the possibilities of a material called germanium. The existence of this semi-conducting material was first predicted by the inventor of the periodic table, Ivanovich Mendeleev. His theory placed the mystery element in the gap in his table between silicon and tin. It was eventually discovered by a German chemist Clemens Winkler, who named the substance after his homeland. However, it was a poor conductor with no apparent use until, in 1945, it was found to be a semi-conductor. The Indian physicist Bose had used a semiconductor as a tuning crystal in those early radio sets and this property proved to be essential in electronics too.

Using a piece of germanium as a base, Kilby printed a complete circuit on it using traces of other elements and produced the first integrated circuit or microchip. The year was 1958 and he had succeeded in eliminating the need for large quantities of connecting wires and started the revolution of the miniaturisation of computing[95]. Another

---

94 Texas Instruments became best known for producing scientific calculators and later the Speak and Spell educational toy.

95 From the beginning of miniaturisation the number of components which can be put on a 'chip' has steadily increased. Moore's Law says that

innovator, Robert Noyce, took this one stage further using much purer silicon. He created a company in 1968 that is still renowned for making computer processors; the globally recognised brand is Intel which is used in the majority of leading computers, both Apple and PC. The first application[96] of integrated circuits was in NASA's Apollo guidance computer. For the first time a computer could fit into box no bigger than a suitcase and weighed less than 30 kilograms. Computers no longer needed to be built on a scale that filled entire rooms and the first steps had been taken to make them available to everyone.

After many successful launches to trial every part of the mission, from the rockets to that guidance computer, the USA were ready to make history. At 9.15am Eastern Daylight Time on July 16th 1969, a Saturn V rocket launched the Apollo 11 mission into space and four days later, on the 20th at 10.56pm Neil Armstrong stepped out onto the moon as 500 million people from across the world watched and heard him say,

'That's one small step for man, and one giant leap for mankind'.

The worldwide broadcast was only possible thanks to the earlier launch of the Telstar communication satellites in 1962 and 1963. This was a planned part of JFK's space program. Bringing the world instant television pictures was clearly important in itself but the satellites had to be in place to preserve for ever the arrival on the moon of the representatives of the Leaders of the Free World.

---

approximately every two years the number of transistors on an integrated circuit will double.

96 The Apollo Guidance System was the first but the only one of its kind. The first mass produced integrated circuit guidance system was for the Minuteman missile (the USA's land launched Intercontinental Nuclear Missile).

Altogether, only twelve men visited the moon on 6 occasions before this period of space exploration came to an end. The final mission brought back a single image that would arguably unite much of the world and spark the environmental movement which followed. That photo was taken on December 7th 1972 by one of the crew of Apollo 17, two hours after the spacecraft left Earth's orbit heading for the moon and 45 000 km from the home. This snapshot of Earth, fully lit by the sun and hanging in space like a blue marble[97] showed our planet as a delicate and finite object. It is one of the most enduring images of Earth and one that was not taken by a computerised satellite but by an astronaut on the last manned flight to the moon.

It is interesting to consider the power of that single still image produced by a technology as old as photography at a time when people were becoming infatuated with the fleeting tv images being broadcast globally and instantly via the Telstar satellites. And it is worth reviewing briefly the amazingly short history of technological advances that brought global communications to this point. Originally radio was transmitted on a line of sight of the transmitter and propagated by repeater stations until amateur enthusiasts realised in the 20s that shorter wavelength waves could be bounced off the ionosphere and transmitted across the globe. Marconi, of course, was the first to make a commercial success of radio broadcasting from the Lizard Peninsula in Cornwall. Radio, along with vast underwater cable networks was the only way to send messages around the world until the end of the Second World War.

The development of TV was necessarily slower,

---

97 A link to the Image -

http://en.wikipedia.org/wiki/File:The_Earth_seen_from_Apollo_17.jpg

beginning in 1926 when John Logie Baird first demonstrated moving images. A limited public service became available in 1929 although the pictures had only 30 lines of resolution until 1935 when the forerunner of BBC 1 gave viewers a choice of 240 or 405 lines and then broadcast only the signal they preferred. So the first format war of the TV and video medium was won by the provider of the higher definition system, none other than Marconi-EMI. The service was stopped at the outbreak of World War II, midway through a Mickey Mouse cartoon, which was the first thing shown when the transmissions resumed after the war.

The press of course was still central to news reporting especially of events in inaccessible places. Mountaineer George Band described the media circus around the 1953 Everest expedition, as 'The Other Everest'. The expedition was sponsored by The Times newspaper which sent out journalist Jan Morris to establish a logistical network from base camp back to London. Paranoid that someone might break the story first, Jan set up a sequence of code words. If her message were intercepted it would appear to be general expedition business and not the real story of success[98]. Jan Morris' code telling The Times the summit had been taken was, "Snow conditions bad. Stop. Advanced base abandoned yesterday. Stop. Awaiting improvement."

This message arrived in London as the nation watched the Coronation of Queen Elizabeth II live on TV.

Less than two decades later, of course, the Telstar satellites made TV broadcasts possible from almost any point on the planet and even from space. Viewers of news and sports events could essentially watch live action, with a

---

98 Jan Morris' book, 'Coronation Everest', details the lengths taken to get the exclusive scoop. Jan was originally James Morris, and possibly one of the first transsexual men to 'come out' and live as a woman.

delay of only a fraction of a second. The assassination of US President John Kennedy, in Dallas, Texas in 1963 happened live in front of an audience of millions and rocked the whole of the Western World. The footage is some of the most watched in history. Compared with the reported news available to previous generations, it is impossible to overestimate the impact on people of watching key events as they happen. The first moon landings, the marriage and funeral of Princess Diana, Michael Jackson's memorial service, the rescue of 33 Chilean miners, the London 2012 Olympic Opening Ceremony and the collapse of the Twin Towers on 9/11 are vivid examples that come to mind[99].

The rapid growth of live broadcasts created a phenomenal appetite for exciting, interesting material to fill airtime. Many sports and activities, never before suited to having spectators, were now welcoming the TV film crew and the audience of thousands watching from the comfort of their own living rooms.

Viewers found rock climbing especially exciting and throughout the sixties, millions turned on their television sets to watch some of the most complex and daring outside broadcasts the BBC[100] had ever carried out. Some commentators have even dubbed these the first 'reality television' shows, where real people were making real life and death decisions all played out live for the TV audience.

In January 1963, there were daily televised updates of the first ascent of the Super-Direct on the North Face of the Cima Grande in the Dolomites. Later that year, an international team of climbers was filmed on an ascent of

---

99 They are also amongst the most seen TV footage in History.

100 Under 2007 downloads there is a paper on 'Reality TV on the Rockface'. http://www.paulgilchrist.net/12.html

the Aiguille Du Midi. This was a somewhat stage managed piece rather than live action filming, as Joe Brown noted in his book *'The Hard Years';*

"Having climbed the first part, we roped down to the bottom during a break in the programme and walked round to the cablelift station to eat and drink. Meanwhile the viewers thought we were still battling our way up the face in a blizzard. When the time came round for the next broadcast we roped down to our new positions higher up the face."

After this success, the BBC commissioned a live programme to be made at Clogwyn du'r Arddu in North Wales called 'Four Men, One Face'. This was broadcast on the 28th September 1963 and the narrators were Guido Magnone, a guide from the Aiguille Du Midi saga, and one Chris Brasher[101]. The Cloggy ascent went out on Grandstand, then the biggest and longest running sports programme in the UK, slotted in between Davis Cup tennis and horseracing. However the weather was poor on the day and some of the better camera angles failed to transmit. In spite of this, the BBC commissioned another programme in 1964 from Kilnsey Crag in North Yorkshire, where a team of four used aid to climb through the *"dizziest and trickiest... most ferocious and sensational overhang in Britain"* and the BBC billed it 'Operation Overhang'.

The following year ITV made its first attempt at capturing climbers in action by filming an ascent of the

---

101 Climber and very talented athlete, Chris's role as Roger Bannister's pacemaker when he achieved the four-minute mile featured in the film Chariots of Fire. Chris later won the 3000m steeplechase gold medal at the 1956 Melbourne Olympics. Three years after setting up his company Brasher Boots in 1978, Chris established the London Marathon, now one of the top five in the world.

route '*Coronation Street*' from Cheddar Gorge. This programme was Chris Bonnington's TV debut and he, Tony Greenbank and Mike Thompson were climbing a route they had 'rehearsed' the previous January. In a bid to justify broadcasting this as a first ascent, Chris pointed out in his second autobiography '*The Next Horizon*' that

'...*we had to show the public how we climbed, but at the same time we had to make it visually interesting, and to do that, we had to be able to climb quickly, to a set schedule.*'

Then, later in 1965, a collaboration between the BBC and Swiss Television was scheduled to coincide with the centenary of Whymper's first ascent of the Matterhorn. The programme was originally conceived as a dramatised documentary, but instead it was decided that a live broadcast should be made. The producers thought it was the '*diciest outside broadcast*' ever attempted. The Head of the BBC Outside Broadcast feared the potential consequences if the climbers were to suffer the same fate as Whymper so he issued a memo insisting the climbers take no unnecessary risks just because they were on TV. That concern proved unfounded and audience feedback said the ascent looked too tame to be a struggle on a mountain with a dangerous reputation. But with 7 million viewers in the UK, some 15% of the population, the show was seen as a breakthrough for televised climbing and the press declared it to be the harbinger of a new age of reality television.

The BBC commissioned another broadcast in 1966 that would push the climbers to their limit. Tom Patey, a celebrated Scottish mountaineer and writer, described it as "*The Greatest Show on Earth*". The aim was to capture a first ascent of a route on Red Walls at Gogarth. This climbing area, discovered only two years previously, is a series of adventurous sea cliffs on Anglesey which already had a terrifying reputation amongst climbers. The first route, also called Gogarth, is still a modern classic and Martin Boysen who, along with Baz Ingle, discovered the Main Cliff recalls.........

"The tide was out when we went down. We just walked along and picked Gogarth as an obvious line, which we could get into at any sort of tides. In fact it was an unfortunate choice because it was incredibly loose at the time..............."

Red Walls is not part of the main cliff though, it is much looser and one of the most serious cliffs to climb on in the UK. The hard red rock is quite friable and interspersed with softer, sandier material where protection can be difficult to arrange and climbers can quickly find themselves in serious positions.

The route planned for the programme is still known as *Television Route* and it is seen by many as a staged ascent where comfort and risk were managed. Whilst fixed pitons and even bolts were placed prior to the ascent, a 10 foot spacing between them kept the level of challenge high for the climbers. Today, most use a safer alternative start but a handful still follow the historic route, where that original line of ironmongery, in a worrying state of decay, marks a line that is now free climbed at E5. Climbing past those rusty stubs entails hanging on to rock which is attached to the neighbouring cliff only by prayer. The fixed gear is little more than archaeological way markers, their integrity eroded by 50 years of maritime air. This was my 100th route at Gogarth and is one I will not forget in a hurry! I can still only wonder what Joe Brown and Royal Robbins were thinking when they made their way up this cliff in full view of the public tuning in on Grandstand.

Before the broadcast, the TV producers and the climbers had no first hand experience of all of this. Keen to create a performance that did not look too easy on camera, no pre-practice was allowed. An entire unclimbed wall was available but the selected route scaled the easiest section to film, although, as history has shown, it was the hardest part to climb. To overcome the difficulties, the route was partly aid climbed by Royal Robins, a star climber, who had been imported from the USA along with much aiding equipment. In the interests of producing a gripping TV programme, the climbers had to relinquish some of the control they were used to having. So it was not long before Joe Brown returned to this imposing sea cliff without the hindrance of a film crew to make first ascents of *Red Wall* and *Wendigo* which are by comparison three star classics on the same cliff.

A year later, the BBC was shipping tons of gear to Hoy, a small island off the Isle of Orkney on the North coast of Scotland. What followed became an historic landmark in the history of both broadcasting and climbing. Six climbers ascended three different routes on the remote Scottish sea stack called The Old Man of Hoy; Joe Brown, Ian MacNaught-Davis, Dougal Haston, Pete Crew, Tom Patey and Chris Bonington. The ascent of the Old Man of Hoy captured the imagination of the audience. But it also showed the way for climbers to forge a new range of careers as professionals, as performers, equipment handlers and safety personnel in precarious locations. On this broadcast, probably for the first time, the level of organisation produced the adventure and drama demanded by the viewers without compromising safety.

Televised live as 'The Great Climb', the broadcast attracted an unprecedented 15 million viewers or around 30% of the UK population. It has been argued that this level of popularity was because public interest in sporting achievement had been provoked by other news at the time. Sir Francis Chichester had successfully sailed single handed around the world in Gypsy Moth IV and had been knighted for achieving one of the last great adventurous firsts just before the Old Man broadcast. Daily news also prompted great hopes for the success of British cyclist Tommy Simpson[102] who was doing well in the Tour De France. The fascination for the public of watching live the tension between success and failure offered by 'reality TV' has been suggested as a factor too.

These reasons are unconvincing and it is surely far more likely that the record breaking viewing figures were because the programme was simply unmissable. Much had been learned from earlier outside broadcasts. This time sections of routes had been pre-practised so that climbers could respond on cue. Fixed lines were in place where needed and camera rehearsals had been carried out. The programme makers understood that watching climbers make calculated risks and deal with potential danger is gripping but tends to happen in short bursts with slow, boring periods in between. So they made the most of the wildly spectacular surroundings. They showcased the engaging personalities of the climbers talking to each other and directly to the viewers in close-up while making light of obvious hazards and perching over breathtaking drops. Skilled and knowledgeable interpretation of every situation was provided by the commentator. The result was legendary.

Climbing suddenly had national stars who were known outside the climbing community. Obviously there were financial rewards and some, Joe Brown[103] and Chris

---

102 Tragically, he died days later on the Mont Ventoux leg from the effects of amphetamines (speed) mixed with alcohol. Abuse of EPOs in cycling is discussed in Chapter 3.

103 Joe climbed the Old Man of Hoy 15 years later for a tv documentary with his teenage daughter Zoe who later became a presenter of the UK cult kids' tv programme Tiswas. Similarly, a young Leo Houlding shot to

Bonington in particular, were able to 'cash in' on their fame just like the stars of any other sport. Climbing was becoming main stream. More people were spurred into taking it up and were boosting the blossoming climbing industry.

The growing participation in climbing was also driven by the social changes of the sixties. There was more money and time to spend on leisure pursuits and the nation's love affair with personal transport in the form of cheaper cars and motorbikes had already begun so travel to crags and mountains was easier for many. National Service ended in 1960 and young people no longer had to spend two of their most active years working in jobs and locations decided by the Ministry of Labour. Government policy greatly increased the numbers in higher education and many students were introduced to climbing through their university or college climbing club. The importance of the guide books that provided inspiration should not be underestimated. Now all the information needed to make the most of visits to the main climbing areas was readily available.

The increased popularity of climbing was reflected in the membership of the British Mountaineering Council. The BMC[104] was established in 1944 by 25 climbing clubs from across the UK to replace the Alpine Club as the national representative body for rock climbers and mountaineers because

"[The Alpine Club] *could never function effectively as such, since its membership was restricted to those respected gentleman with a good Alpine background.*"

Created to be open to all "*regardless of race, religion or*

---

fame early in his career when he climbed the Old Man for kids' tv programme Blue Peter.

104 http://www.thebmc.co.uk/a-brief-history-of-the-bmc

political party", in the early days, individuals did not join as members in their own right. They were members because they belonged to clubs which were affiliated and, at the beginning of the fifties, 35 clubs constituted the BMC. But the growth in the numbers of people taking up climbing and forming new clubs was such that by the end of seventies there were 237 affiliated clubs and an additional three thousand individual members. Today the BMC has over 300 clubs and around 70 000 members.

One of the first publications of the Council was the only instructional manual available at the time; *"Climbing in Britain"* by John Barford. Such was the demand for straight forward information on safety in the hills and the use of climbing gear that by the early sixties it had sold a staggering 120 000 copies. To meet demand, a second handbook was commissioned. Published in 1966, this seminal work, "Mountaineering; from Hillwalking to Alpine Climbing" by Alan Blackshaw was still in print in 1978.

Undoubtedly, the development of outdoor education played its part in increasing the numbers who enjoyed the hills of the UK. In particular, one man stands out in its history, Kurt Hahn. A German educator of Jewish upbringing, he opposed the Nazi party and was imprisoned until the British Prime Minister appealed for his release. With the help of Geoffrey Winthrop-Young, Hahn escaped to the UK and in 1934 he helped set up Gordonstoun School in Scotland where the education was based on his belief that learning through experiences outside the classroom should predominate. In 1940 he further developed the ethos of education with the outdoors at its heart by establishing the first Outward Bound Centre in Aberdovey, Wales. Now Outward Bound is a major international provider of outdoor education. Following this lead, the first local authority outdoor education centre, White Hall, was opened in Derbyshire in 1950. Others followed and, in response to a growing need for instructors, the BMC and the Central Council for Physical Recreation established the Mountain Leader Training Boards in 1964 and set up nationally recognised qualifications. More children were brought into contact with the great outdoors and unsurprisingly many continued with climbing, mountaineering and hillwalking as adults. Today the experience of learning outdoors is embedded in the UK's National Curriculum.

Another indicator of the growing numbers engaged in outdoor activities was the need to provide a rescue service. The first call for organised mountain rescue came as long ago as 1903 when four climbers who were roped together all fell to their deaths on Scafell. Rudimentary first aid and rescue equipment began to be made available and a group was formed which included the famous climbers A. S. Piggot and Morley Wood. They took on the task of redesigning a stretcher for use in mountain terrain and went on to set up a national First Aid Committee of Mountaineering Clubs in 1936 funding it from a 2% levy from each club.

A member of the committee, Wilson Hey was a climber who was also a doctor at Manchester Royal Infirmary. He realised the importance of immediate pain relief when he received an injured climber more than five hours after an accident and later announced,

"The absence of morphia with the transport had done more damage to the limb than the mountain."

Hey's unshakable determination to make adequate pain relief available resulted in an unprecedented stand-off with the Government. Refused permission by the Home Office to issue morphine to rescue posts, he supplied it at his own expense from 1934 until 1949. Prosecuted for not keeping a dangerous drugs record and facing a large fine and prison sentence, he was eventually convicted of a lesser offence and fined only £10. Within days, a remarkable u-turn by the Home Office produced a request for Hey to put forward a plan to issue pain relief to rescue posts. The model he came up with is still very familiar to today's rescue teams. The First Aid Committee became the Mountain Rescue Committee in 1950 and voluntary teams now serve every mountain area in the UK and deal with the ever increasing number of 'call outs' or requests for rescue[105].

As the numbers participating in mountain based sports increased, inevitably so did the number of businesses set up to exploit this growing market. Some specialised in manufacturing equipment while others specialised in selling it. One of the earliest outdoor shops was established in 1933. Brigham's originally supplied cycling and walking boots, their trademark being bespoke climbing boots with the customer's personalised pattern of nails in the sole. After World War II, the shop kept up with the demands of the growing numbers of climbers by selling them readily available war surplus stock. As recently as 1955, when more climbers from the UK started to explore the Alps, Frederick Brigham headed over looking for sources of alpine equipment and he began to import Italian boots and French climbing hardware. Under the name of Fredrick's son, Ellis Brighams is familiar to today's customers and is still one of the leading shops for all mountain sports from skiing to climbing.

The fame of other shops also spread. The Roger Turner Mountain Shop in Nottingham was a focal point for climbers in the area and Joe Brown opened his first

---

105 The number of incidents rose slowly and steadily until the mid 1990s when the use of mobile phones greatly increased the number of callouts for non-serious injuries.

shop in Llanberis in 1966. One of my first jobs in North Wales was in this famous outdoor store in the late 1990s where I was fascinated to find, in an upstairs room, relics from bygone days when Joe and his staff used to make their own slings and harnesses and trial prototype pieces of gear for people who fancied themselves as inventors. One was intended to be an alternative for the figure of eight descender which looked like a cross between Abu Hamza's claw and a ship's anchor. It was intended to be used as an abseil device but the rope tended to unwrap when descending so it was shelved.

Even more alarming was a device to simplify retrieving the rope after abseiling which was an elaborate hook, clamp and spring system that, once weighted, would lock onto a sling at the top of the abseil. Crucially, the climber had to keep the rope weighted all the way down. An accidental encounter with an unseen ledge for instance would unweight the rope and the device would automatically unlock. The rope, the prototype device and the climber would then plummet to the ground. If lucky enough to survive the fall, the climber would almost certainly receive fatal head injuries from 2kg of metal following closely behind at terminal velocity. Clearly this invention too was destined to failure. As far as I could tell, not one of this collection of antique and essentially useless items of gear ever got to the production stage mostly because they were deadly. But I was always impressed by the detailed care taken and the intricacy of the mechanisms showed how determined people were to develop the next 'big thing'.

Then, as now, the market for climbing equipment was growing, and gear was being produced to meet the demand. The Union International Alpine Association (UIAA) which had been in existence since 1932, recognised the need for equipment to meet agreed safety standards. In 1960 they initiated a project to bring that about. In the meantime, climbers continued with their own original ways to test the equipment they were making. Snowdonia Mouldings made climbing helmets to a pattern devised by Joe Brown when instructing at the Whitehall Outdoor Centre. The product was tested by sending the wearer of a helmet outside to have rocks dropped on their head by someone from an upstairs window! The days when climbers searched for suitable pebbles and made their own rope slings had been consigned to history and the choice of clever devices was proliferating rapidly. Now a climber can walk into a shop and buy from a vast array of gear confident that every item will meet the twenty different standards required for personal protective equipment. This is thanks to the UIAA whose efforts finally established the first internationally approved standards in 1965. Then all they needed was a memorably unique logo which would become the instantly recognised symbol for climbing safety worldwide. So one of the members of the committee asked his young son to draw a mountain and added the circle and the letters UIAA which still form the emblem every climber looks for before getting out the plastic.[106]

At the beginning of the 1960s, the equipment available was limited mainly to specialist rock climbing shoes, or PA's, chocks and nylon rope which were all contributing to the safety of the sport. But the development of a piece of equipment which would prove to be a breakthrough was imminent; the climbing harness. If it seems surprising that it took so long to produce what is an absolute essential for modern climbers then it is worth reminding

---

106 In European the bureaucrats have taken over and produce CE marking for 'personal protection equipment' (PPE), which seem to essentially be similar to the UIAA markings but probably cost the tax payer considerably more.

ourselves that until this point climbers made 'waistlines' of a few loops of rope tied round themselves. These were intended only to prevent a fall being fatal since the guiding tenet of the time was that the leader simply did not fall. The techniques taken for granted now which make the harness indispensible either did not exist then or they were used rarely, sometimes only in extremis. The abseil for example involved maximising friction by wrapping the rope around the body and leg. It was used only if absolutely necessary and never as a conveniently quick way of descending a rock route. The classic body belay worked in much the same way, was used universally and often resulted in scorched hands and melted waterproofs. Comfort was not an issue. The climber's weight would normally never come onto the waistline.

Against this background, Tony Howard[107] credits Brian Stokes with designing the first harness and it was made from leather. This spread the load over a wider area than the rope loops, making it more comfortable. It also allowed the chocks which were becoming more commonly used to be carried on a racking system at the waist rather than over the shoulder with a bandolier. As the textile mills around the Peak District closed down, the old leather belts used to power the machinery were abundant, cheap and readily available. It was the ideal material for the purpose and, with the addition of a sling used in a figure of eight as leg loops, the sit harness was born. After using one on his landmark ascent of Troll Wall in 1965, Tony Howard improved the design and began to sell it as the Troll Mark II. Used on the Old Man of Hoy broadcast, the Troll Mark II harness benefitted greatly from this early instance of product placement and every climber in the TV audience immediately wanted one.

107

http://www.mtnforum.org/sites/default/files/harness_development.pdf

Troll[108] was the collaboration of Tony Howard and Alan Waterhouse and the simplicity of their next new piece of climbing equipment was pure genius. They used nylon webbing or tape to manufacture slings and the Troll Mark 2 nylon waist belt. They also made 'Wedges', another form of chockable protection, and nylon tape ladders called etriers for aid climbing. The Mark II harness design lasted until 1970 when Don Whillans came to the factory with a new idea to develop a nylon 'nappy' that supported the climber's weight more effectively. These were a great step forward in comfort but any male climber who, like me, has ever used one will know that they had a major design flaw. A thin piece of   tape came up and over one's manhood and more than one set of plums have been caught by the full force of a fall. Even so, this continued to be the harness of choice for many years.

The design of the Troll Whillans' harness was revolutionary but it also received the media attention and celebrity endorsement which brought guaranteed success. It appeared in photographs, on TV and featured in lectures after being supplied to Chris Bonington's 1970 Annapurna Expedition. In Bonington's book '*Annapurna South Face*' he described the Whillans' harness as,

'an outstanding success, for it enabled one to rest back in the seat while jumaring up snow slopes.'

Three years later, the same harness was used on

---

108 Until 1977, most climbers used one or two karabiners clipped directly to the protection then Troll invented the quick draw. Very handy, but my favourite Troll product was the vibrant climbing pants they made in the late 80s and early 90s; truly a fashion crime, these belong in the past along with fluorescent socks and bright lycra tights.

another Bonington expedition, this time to the South-West Face of Everest. This attempt was unsuccessful but the second attempt in 1975 did succeed. The accolades received by the makers of the harness once again resonated through the climbing world; Chris Bonington said that all the members of the team thought they were the best in the world.

Peter Hutchinson was another great kit innovator. He not only made chromoly pegs but his company Mountain Equipment more famously made down clothing. The business captured the attention of Yvon Chouinard who invited Peter to join him in making down equipment, but financial difficulties caused Yvon to pull out at the last minute. A Welsh climbing company sprang up at that time; Clogwyn Climbing Gear. Better known as Clog, it went through many incarnations after being established by Denny Moorhouse. Armed with the engineering knowledge he had learned with Peter Hutchinson, Denny began manufacturing aluminium karabiners and regular hexagonal nuts in 1967 and started to see some success. But it had been an uphill journey. Denny had been undeterred by the bankruptcy of one of his original companies and used to sneak into his foreclosed factory unit at night to make equipment for the new business he was trying to set up. Eventually, after Clog and International Safety Systems, Denny established Denny Moorhouse Mountaineering in 1981. That company became DMM and is still a globally recognised brand with a reputation for innovative design. Their early lightweight karabiners were like much of their kit today; world leading in terms of functionality, weight, aesthetics and strength.

Across the Atlantic, Yvon Chouinard and his business partner Tom Frost were also developing equipment to suit the style of climbing in the US. Chouinard was the practically minded son of a French-Canadian handyman and in 1957 he bought a coal fired forge and taught himself to make hardened steel pitons. Initially he sold these from the back of his car but they were so popular that he set up Chouinard Equipment Ltd. After an ice climbing trip to the European Alps and venturing up some ice gullies in his beloved Sierra Nevada in the late 60s, he turned his hand to improving the crampon, ice axe and ice screws. He made the crampons stiff so that they would not flex when the front points were driven into steep snow. He made the pick of the axe hold in ice more reliably and he not only increased the cross sectional area of the ice screws but made them lighter too. It was then the usual practice to climb up ice by cutting steps and handholds using the adze of the ice axe. Chouinard's radical modifications made this technique obsolete at a stroke. Now a climber could kick the front points of the crampons into the ice and stand on them and swing the axes to make placements with the points of the picks. In short, the sport of ice climbing was changed to what it is today.

Chouinard Equipment has since become Black Diamond and in 1972 the sister company was established, Patagonia. This is the clothing company which specialised from the first in rugged technical outdoor wear and still leads the field today. Both are successful outdoor companies but both are also world leaders in environmental and working practices. In his book 'Let My People Go Surfing', Yvon Chouinard explains his philosophy. Among other things, his was one of the first businesses to open an on-site healthy cafeteria, offer child care and arrange various environmental and activity groups for its workers. Chouinard later pledged the greater of 1% of sales or 10% of profits 'for the planet'[109]; an annual

---

109 The company has bought vast areas of the Patagonia region and is active in reforestation, reintroduction of indigenous species and working

donation to environmental activism in other words. The company was already making fleece clothing from recycled bottles when an audit in the 1990s showed that cotton was the most environmentally damaging material they used. So Patagonia switched to use only pesticide free cotton which, according to some, raised demand sufficiently to bring about the creation of California's organic cotton industry. The Chouinard companies have been at the cutting edge of environmental protection since the early seventies and an exemplar for businesses worldwide.

Concerned about the effects climbing was having on the planet, Yvon Chouinard had noticed the extent of damage from the placement and removal of thousands of pegs from classic routes on the cracks in Yosemite. This was so bad that numerous routes sport 'peg scars' which are still visible today. A striking example is *Serenity Cracks* which I set out to repeat with a local climber on my first trip there. Sadly we were rained off the continuation into *Sons of Yesterday* but I vividly remember the first pitch where a crack appears from below a thin seam and cuts a more or less direct line up the cliff. Having got to the front of the queue for this classic route, the detail becomes obvious. It looks as if someone has chipped small shallow square holes all the way up the crack. In places they are just inches apart and it is possible to pinch between these peg scars or carefully use them as toe holds. Occasionally the scars are so big that they provide placements for protection. The wall is otherwise smooth and ironically it would not be possible to free climb it if it had not once been pegged to death.

It was Royal Robbins who introduced the technique which made a revolutionary change possible. He returned

---

towards a National Park. It is also involved in other schemes worldwide and in the US.

from the UK after filming the *Television Route* on Red Walls in 1967 with what was probably the first set of chocks to appear in the USA which he had bought from Joe Brown's shop in Llanberis. Robbins and his wife Liz put up *Nutcracker* in Yosemite, on a cliff just below the imposing El Cap. He took neither a hammer nor any pegs and used only those nuts for protection and he published an article entitled '*Nuts and You*' for the US climbing audience at about the same time.

Robbins' friend and climbing partner, Chouinard, quickly took an interest in this new form of protection and in 1971 he made some nuts with an irregular hexagonal shape called 'hexentrics'. These were similar in shape to the machine nuts of old. This was no coincidence, the first ever nuts had been diligently searched out beside the Snowdon Railway for the same reason; this shape seemed to fit most cracks. But Chouinard's new hexentrics could be placed in two different ways because the lengths of the sides of the hexagon varied whilst the symmetry was preserved. Then a Norwegian climber called Tomas Carlstrom made a mistake when he was trying to machine hexentrics of his own design from hexagonal nuts made by Clog. The result was a totally asymmetric shape which fitted into cracks in three different ways so he passed this design to Chouinard who began marketing them in 1974.

Two years later, awareness of the damage caused by pegging was growing and Tom Frost wrote another piece in Summit magazine called '*Preserving the Cracks*'[110]. He used images of *Serenity Crack* to make the point that over pegging was destroying the rock. He tackled fears about

---

110 Link to super topos where an scan of the article can be found along with images of Serenity Cracks.

http://www.supertopo.com/tr/Preserving-The-Cracks-Tom-Frost-Makes-His-Case-AAJ-1972/t145n.html safety by showing that nuts and hexes were stronger than the karabiners they were attached to and that their wedge design did not allow them to rotate out of cracks like pegs sometimes did. He made a strong case that attitudes should change, that ascents protected solely by nuts were possible and that climbers should leave routes clean of gear. The article was influential and ethics in the US did begin to change. More climbers started to accept that some pegs should be left in situ on long routes and it became usual to ascend shorter routes without using a hammer. Tom Frost dubbed this 'clean climbing' and it is still being developed today as climbers try to make hammerless ascents of El Cap and other Big Wall routes, rather than nail their way to the top. Many El Cap routes are now given two grades; an A grade for climbing with pegs and a C grade for climbing clean without a hammer.

For me, there is one particularly memorable quote from Frost's article because it is about Joe Brown. His name was also famous in the US and this instance exemplifies his personal standards and makes an important point about British ethics;

"Of all the challenges presented over the years by Welsh Rock, only Cenotaph Corner approached this wall in its compelling demand to be climbed. Brown had tried his utmost to climb it with the minimum of aid, but had retreated rather than use more pegs than his exacting standards allowed.

One outstanding unclimbed section of cliff appeared so hard that bolts seemed the only solution: the right hand side of Great Wall [on Cloggy]. *But it was widely felt at the time* [and indeed still is] *that bolting this wall would be a terrible desecration of the crag and represent a threat to the whole delicate basis of British free climbing."*

Ten years later, in 1986, that wish to uphold ethical purity led to Johnny Dawes' seemingly impossible bolt free first ascent of *The Indian Face* on that very same blank section of Great Wall on Cloggy. The route weighed in at E9 and nearly thirty years on it has still only had three ascents due to the certainty of a ground fall from around 40m for a leader who blew the crux. With this achievement, Dawes had pushed forward the limit of what is possible and made the emphatic statement that the limit depends only on dedication and talent.

The evolution of the last true innovation in climbing protection began in the early 1970s with the invention of the *Friend* or camming unit. The credit is usually given to Ray Jardine, who along with Wild Country designed, built and manufactured the first commercially available cams but the history of these amazing pieces of engineering and their forerunners is an interesting one.

The curve of a cam, circular at one end and elliptical at the other, commonly occurs in nature. The mathematics of the curve has been marvelled at for at least eight centuries. Leonardo Fibonacci first noticed nature's progression and derived the number sequence it determines. Named after him, the sequence can be plotted into the logarithmic spiral found in shells, pinecones, storms, nebulae and the way leaves grow around the stem of a plant. Leonardo da Vinci used nature's preferred form of spiral in the detail of many of his paintings, particularly locks of hair. Back in 1863, Descartes described it mathematically as an expression of uniform growth.

The cam shape has been used through the ages in engineering to change the direction of movement. The fixed cam on a shaft has long been the arrangement which transforms circular rotation of the shaft into a linear up and down movement which can be used to drive pistons for example. If a cam is threaded on a loop of cord through the centre of the circular part and placed in a crack, then weighting the cord pulls the circular edge downwards against one side of the crack while the edge of the elliptical part pushes upwards against the opposite side. While the cord is loaded downwards, the opposing sideways forces hold the cam in the crack.

Two designers first came up with the idea of using the principle of camming in climbing protection. One was the Russian climber and gear designer Vitaly Abalakov[111] and the other was the American climber, Greg Lowe. Abalakov's version resembled the modern tri-cam in that it used the force of any load to cam it into place. Lowe's design incorporated a rudimentary spring and was more akin to a modern camming device although it had only one pair of cams opposing a solid bar. It was Ray Jardine, a systems analyst with a *'questioning mind and a passion for climbing'* who eventually came up with a four cam spring-loaded device. He worked for the Martin Marietta Corporation, a major US aerospace and weapons system manufacturer. Jardine was an engineer and some claim he worked for NASA which is possible since he developed space flight computer simulations at Martin Marietta[112]. Anyway, he came up with a most scientifically interesting piece of climbing protection.

---

111 Abalakov is best known for his technique for making anchors in ice. Two holes are bored into the ice to make a continuous V-shaped tunnel which is threaded with cord or tape.

112 The Martin Marietta Corporation was successfully sued by Ida Phillips under Title VII of the Civil Rights Act 1964. The company denied her employment because of their policy not to employ mothers with pre-school children. The Act's eleven Titles included, equal rights to vote, the outlawing of discrimination on the grounds of race, colour, religion, sex or nationality, the end to segregation in schools and the right to move civil rights cases from state courts with all white juries and biased judges to federal courts.

The early cams were a completely new concept. Chocks and hexes could only be placed in cracks which tapered at the bottom. When pulled downwards, they jammed instead of falling out. Cams on the other hand, could be placed in parallel-sided or even slightly flared cracks and they could be placed very quickly. The laws of mechanics and vector forces dictate that roughly every kilogram pulling downwards on the stem of the cam produced a force equal to two kilograms pushing outwards on the walls of the crack. As the force of a fall increased so did the force holding the device in place.

Jardine's version uses four sprung cams which stay open as wide as possible and pivot about an axle so that each cam can adjust to the shape of a crack like a car's suspension adapts to the road. Those cams are linked to a trigger on a stem to close them together when placing or removing the unit. Once in the crack, releasing the trigger allows the cams to spring open and the device cannot be pulled out again without using the trigger to close them. Now the climber clips the rope with a karabiner to a tape sling at the end of the stem. Whilst these units do have limitations, the plain fact is that their first appearance opened up a whole new array of routes in places where it had previously been impossible to arrange protection without resorting to bolting.

Having come up with the initial design, Jardine needed to determine the camming angle which is the angle between opposing cams when they pivot. Too acute and they would not grip, too wide and the size would not vary enough. Going back to the basics of friction, Ray placed a polished block of aluminium on a polished piece of granite like that in Yosemite. The slab of rock was tilted to an angle of 18 degrees before the block slipped. The angle therefore had to be less than that so 15 degrees was chosen. Then Ray went to England to visit Mark Vallance who ran Wild Country, the company waiting to manufacture the cams. Together they discovered that the 15 degree angle which worked so superbly on Yosemite granite was not shallow enough to grip on other types of rock. It was not quite 'back to the drawing board' but a rapid adjustment had to be made before Friends[113] were released onto the market to become essential gear for every climber on every type of rock.

The extent to which camming units changed the world of traditional climbing is best illustrated by the history of the sea cliff, Gogarth. A Mecca for trad climbing in the UK, the crag has been at the forefront of activity since the sixties. In the two years before Friends were released in 1978, an average of only 8 new routes were established annually but nearly 70 routes were climbed in the first year after they came on the market. Development in the Llanberis Pass shows a similar leap forward. A guidebook to each of these areas had been published the year before which would have boosted the popularity of the crags but does not explain the remarkable spike in the number of new routes. The difficulty of the climbs also rose significantly which needs a full discussion later.

The influence of the Friend in the USA was even more obvious. One climbing area where the ability to place protection in parallel cracks made colossal numbers of routes possible was the desert of Utah, in particular Indian Creek. Here there are   thousands of parallel sided cracks

---

113 Originally this was Ray's code word for his devices which had to be top secret until 1978 when they were displayed on tv in 'Tomorrow's World" on the BBC. A complete history can be found in the Wild Country Cam Book.

http://www.wildcountry.co.uk/download/files/2010-11_Catalogues/V1146_Wild_Cam_book_v602.pdf which often run uninterrupted at the same width for their entire length. Steve 'Crusher' Bartlett in his book '*Desert Tower*' said,

"*Nowhere would Jardine's invention have such an impact as the desert... Camming devices turned previously dangerous parallel cracks into amusement-park-safe excursions.*"

I visited Indian Creek briefly in 2009 and can only support this view. The rack my partner and I turned up with had at least three cams of each size and would be regarded as substantial at home. But here we were woefully ill equipped like gunfighters with sticks. At mid-week no one else was around and we only learned later that weekend climbers who travel to the area swap and share cams to suit the width of the crack they are climbing. So rather than three cams of the same size they often carry 10 or more. Sadly, we were extremely limited in the routes we could climb and missed out on many three star classics. With so little gear, those we did were not the amusement park rides we had been promised even if they were safer and more fun for us than for the climbers who made the first ascents in the days before cams. One of the routes I was gutted to miss out on was the hands and fists *Supercrack*[114] which was identified in 1971 but not climbed until 1976 by Earl Wiggin using hexes. The route was seen as so bold and so hard at the time that a fall would have been potentially fatal. But just two years later, this and other routes were transformed by the invention of the Friend.

Bartlett had not understated the impact of the new form of protection in Yosemite where Ray Jardine had originally developed the cams. It seems fitting that their inventor was the first to climb *Separate Reality*. A sought

---

114 Video of first ascent of Supercrack -

http://www.youtube.com/watch?v=xO8ZPrFvqWQ

after prize, this hard route of only 20m with a 6m crack that cuts its way through a roof would only have been possible before with large pegs or chocks preplaced from above. Ray was successful using Friends but technically he could not claim the first ascent since he apparently had a rest on the route.

A year after the successful release of Friends, Mark Vallance and Wild Country turned their attention to perfecting the nut. This was not the fundamentally new concept represented by Friends but a refinement of the tried and tested chock. Their experiments produced a nut with one concave face and one convex face which was almost identical to the set of rocks which hangs from the harness of every climber today. With that, the evolution of our modern climbing equipment was pretty much complete.

The sixties saw the ultimate adventure and the most determined push against the limits of what was deemed possible that could ever be imagined; representatives of the human race left our planet and travelled in space. For billions, it happened in real time through the TV or radio and everyone who saw or heard it was changed by the experience. If it had not happened, we would not see our Earth as we do now. It sparked technologies which made the world smaller whilst expanding the personal horizons of everyone living then and now. The rapidly growing sport of climbing and the climbers themselves were not immune to the belief that all individuals, not just the privileged, could achieve anything with the right technology. So in the sixties and seventies gear was produced which could protect hitherto impossible lines without destroying the environment or the rock or the challenge for climbers of the future. That challenge had already been accepted by the few who realised the steep, apparently holdless routes that would take climbing to the next level required superhuman strength and a prima ballerina's ability to execute intricate series of moves. These visionaries began the next revolution; they honed their skills on artificial surfaces like brick walls, they built fitness on pull-up bars and they worked on their moves indoors. Ignoring accusations of cheating from diehards, the new wave of elite climbers were training specifically for climbing!

What training did for climbers and climbing is the focus of the last chapter along with the birth of indoor climbing and what the present and possibly what the future might hold for climbing. However before we reach that conclusion we are going to explore the seemingly unanswerable question of why anybody would willingly risk life and limb in the pursuit of a sport. Where we look at the psychology of risk taking and the science behind what might make some of us tick.

7 AN EXPLORATION OF RISK

Previous chapters detail how science and technology have affected our lives in general as well as the sport of climbing in particular. Arguably the single force that drove all scientific development was introduced in the first chapter which explored curiosity as the motivation for learning. Without that, could humanity have even begun to explore the realms of science we now take for granted? That incessant, insatiable human curiosity produced an extraordinary understanding of the natural sciences and the determination and skills to harness them to make our own incredible technologies.

This curiosity has not been exclusively directed outwards. Recent generations have held up a mirror to themselves to examine the driving force behind all innovation; the human mind. When we climbers turn that mirror on ourselves what can we learn about why we climb? I do not intend to enter into the world of philosophy and the more existential question why we are here. The question that fascinates me is why some of us possess an urge to take undue chances with our lives in our modern risk adverse society.

Trying to find an answer was incredibly hard, necessarily involving neuroscience, genetics and psychology. A PhD thesis on just one facet of this research would normally take three years so summarising it all into a concise and readable story proved challenging. Add to the mix that very little of the research is totally infallible so some of my theories and the links I make are contentious. What I have tried to do is give an honest, open and enquiring look at all areas of the research and where possible highlight those areas of contention.

If you are a climber or a mountaineer, pause for a minute and try to answer this simple question; Why do you climb? The chances are that it seems to be such a large and vital part of your life that you struggle to know where to start to frame a simple answer. But it is probably easier if I ask; How does climbing make you feel?

Personally, I climb because it makes me happy. I believe I feel like that because I become so absorbed with the act of climbing that I forget about bills, deadlines, worries and other worldly things. It just becomes me and the rock. Clearly I do it to try to escape ordinary life temporarily. That says something about my personality as we shall see. But we will also see that it produces physical effects too. The fact that I find it enjoyable may be due to the natural response in my brain; possibly producing a 'natural high'.

There are essentially three schools of thought developing in research into risk taking;

School 1 - when taking risks we may become addicted to the sensations and feelings we experience.

School 2 – assumes risk has a more functional purpose and asks what benefit   risk taking gives to a person taking chances.

School 3 – takes the view that personality and/or genetics play a role in predisposing individuals to taking risks.

Clearly, these schools of thought apply only to the principal reasons for the behaviour of large groups of risk takers. The decision making that leads a particular individual, such as you or I, to engage in risky activity is an unquantifiable and complex process which depends on personality,   genetics,   upbringing   and   current circumstances. And we should be under no illusion. There is a darker side to taking risks and some of us might prefer not to look too closely at why we sometimes put ourselves in danger. Perhaps instead we should try to remember that it does not really matter why we climb except because we enjoy it and that is probably all that counts.

However, risk taking as a facet of the behaviour of groups of people is fascinating and the scientific investigation of those ideas is enlightening. Research into risk-based sports is proliferating but it is by no means wide spread. So occasionally my arguments are drawn from more general research into what might be seen as less socially acceptable risk-taking pastimes such as serial murder and international banking. You will have to judge for yourself whether you think they can justifiably be applied here.

In any case, it makes sense to give ourselves an historical context and we should obviously begin with one of the most often repeated quotes from any climber or mountaineer about why we climb; George Mallory's *'...because it's there'*. As it stands, it offers very little as an explanation of why he chose to risk his life to satisfy curiosity about the possibility of surviving one of the world's most extreme environments.

Today it is generally accepted that risk taking only very rarely adds to the sum total of human knowledge. We climb for much more intrinsic reasons and it can be argued that climbing done well and in control by experts has become safer than ever. But from my five years serving on the Llanberis Mountain Rescue Team looking after one small area of mountains in North Wales, I can assure you that climbing is neither safe, nor bothered if you are an expert or a novice. Bad things do happen to nice people and most climbers accept that as part of the sport they love.

'Because it's there' then is arguably more of a maxim of the time. It was not until ten years after Tenzing and

Hillary stood on the summit of Everest that a young psychologist, James Lester, started some of the earliest research into risk takers in mountaineering. A member of the Peace Corps, he joined the 1963 American Everest Expedition and reached a height of 6700m (22000 feet). His mission was not to summit but to observe and study how the climbing team dealt with high levels of stress and how they gelled together. It was James Lester[115] who truly began to formulate an answer to the question posed to Mallory.

Lester's expedition profile report was written early in his career. He maintained this lifelong interest well into his retirement, extending the research by reviewing as many of the great works of mountaineering literature as he could. He abstracted from them quotes that would express the meanings the climbers found in what they did. In the introduction to his article he confesses that,

"'Because it is there', ...could never satisfy someone with a psychological bent'.

His original task of profiling the American Everest climbers to see how they acted in 'stressful' situations provided the earliest indicators of common attributes amongst those who enjoyed this type of lifestyle. Firstly, the team had a much bigger proportion of assertive people than an age and educationally matched control group and Lester observed that they........

---

115 James Lester wrote two noteworthy articles. The first was about his experience of the expedition and what he saw as the personality traits/motivations of the climbers for engaging in high risk sport; 'Wrestling With Self on Mount Everest' Journal of Humanistic Psychology 1983. The second was a review of 150 years of mountain literature which reflects modern research on the subject; 'Spirit, Identity and Self in Mountaineering' Journal of Humanistic Psychology 2004.

"........expressed considerable restlessness, dislike for routine, desire for autonomy, tendency to be dominant in personal relations, a lack of interest in social interaction for its own sake. Their felt need for achievement and independence was very high, while their felt need for intimacy and affection was low."

Further, Lester reported that,

"Ordinary domestic lives were more stressful to the average team member than were the icy conditions in a fragile tent on a snowy ridge in a high wind with inadequate oxygen."

He also heard the climbers mention that they felt more at home and more themselves whilst on the expedition and that it provided them with an escape from mundane domestic routines and schedules.

Just from these few paragraphs then, Lester has already suggested that escapism is one benefit of risk taking and that climbers are more likely to be dominant personalities and less likely to need intimacy and affection. These two themes were later to be researched experimentally with regards to the function they might fulfil and the benefits they might provide.

In his later review of mountain literature Lester elaborated on those initial observations. He identified these eight threads of meaning shared by climbers;

Contact with a High Power
A Sense of Freedom
A Sense of Power, Energy and Vitality
Contact with a Better Self
Assertion of Self
The Conquest of Self
Escape from Self
Unity

Several of these themes can arguably be linked. In particular, those involving self sit more comfortably with the theory, explored later in this chapter, that risk taking performs an emotional function. But the first four threads seem to fit the notion that a 'natural high' may be involved in risk taking that may have resulted in the literal interpretations Lester found. The science which supports them was developed subsequently but next I want to share with you what Lester unearthed.

To start with we will look at what Lester referred to as *Contact with a High Power*. This was something he had hoped to observe on the 1963 expedition and is the term he gave to an experience where transcendence is reached. Key words he reportedly looked for in the literature were infinity, eternity, ecstasy, reverence, salvation and humility. These experiences were often associated with the most extreme of survival situations. Whilst Lester's first paper on the 1963 expedition did not report any such experiences, his subsequent correspondence with some of the team, who after summiting had been benighted at 8500m (28000ft), are a chilling read;

"When we bivouacked that night I was much clearer in the things that counted to me, than in recalling time, temperature, etc. That was a destruction of what I understood when I had to relate that junk into a foolish microphone. I could see my body lying on that rock and snow, but that didn't matter. I cared not if I came back, for life had been found (again – not the first time I felt that) which transcended mere physical survival. I knew we would survive anyway."

Another climber later wrote this of the same situation high on the mountain,

"There was no space, no time, no sense of losing life. It did not matter whether this type of life was lost or not, for life as I knew it then transcended all physical manifestations of body. I was looking over the arête into the other side of the universe…"

As we will see, this incident could be ascribed as much to a euphoric high brought about by the extreme danger the pair overcame as to some quasi-religious experience.

This description resembles another of the recurrent themes in Lester's paper, the *Sense of Freedom* which allows the world to be experienced in a new way. He quotes Reinhold Messner after his successful solo ascent of Everest without oxygen;

"The summit seemed so peaceful to me and the descent so unimportant, as if I meant nothing to myself, as if I had climbed out of a sea of loneliness into the safety of the universe".

We probably have to accept that in those moments Messner and those from Lester's expedition were undoubtedly at the extreme hypoxic limit of human endeavour. People tested at altitude in hyperbaric chambers can become so delirious from lack of oxygen that they can forget to reattach themselves to the supplementary supply. Often they fail to execute the most basic of tasks and try, for example, to put square blocks in the round holes of a toy.

Whether the *Contact with a High Power* or the *Sense of Freedom* are experienced independently or are just tricks of the hypoxic mind needs to be considered. Climbers certainly experience serenity after climbing routes sometimes. Usually the feelings are linked with the most challenging of survival situations which brings up the question of whether transcendence is part of a death defying experience or simply the human body's natural reaction to risk-taking and fear. Whilst I have never had a truly religious experience neither have I faced what I believed would be certain death. What I have felt many times when climbing is an inner peace which brings a greater sense of place where the world looks more vibrant and colourful than before the climb. These times are usually associated with the hardest and most challenging routes I have ever climbed.

The next thread of meaning from Lester's list is the

Sense of Power, Energy and Vitality. This sounds similar to the adrenaline-driven physical and mental jolt we all recognise as naked fear and which is technically well known as the 'flight or fight' response to moments of real or apparent danger. In such moments we can find ourselves fuelled with a previously unknown energy and clarity epitomised by John Muir's,

"... *when life blazed forth... I seemed to suddenly become possessed of a new sense*", and Dougal Haston's,

"*Now the iron was returning to my soul; I was rediscovering that feeling of inner invincibility that I had felt on the descent of Everest. Had the climbing not been so utterly demanding, I could not have felt this way*".

This would certainly support the contention of the mainstream media that extreme sportsmen and women are adrenalin junkies.

If then climbers climb to experience those sensations and feelings mentioned above then there should be a scientific explanation for them and to a certain extent that exists. The explanation lies in the neuroscientific understanding of fear; in layman's terms, what goes on in our brain when we scare ourselves which is something we climbers can regularly achieve.

Fear starts in an area known as the amygdala, a walnut sized area in the centre of the brain just above the spinal cord whose primary purpose seems to be to deal with both memory and emotional responses. Once the emotional and physical responses induced by fear are sensed in the amygdala, it sends messages to other parts of the brain by releasing several neurotransmitter chemicals[116] amongst which are dopamine, endorphins and noradrenalin. These

---

116 This section is highlighted here:

http://www.psychologytoday.com/blog/the-playing-field/200803/the-addictive-nature-adrenaline-sport are the major neurotransmitters. Each has different functions and symptoms but all are part of the 'flight or fight' response; one of evolution's greatest gifts. What follows outlines how it works but not necessarily in the order in which it happens in the brain.

The trigger is the cascade of hormones and neurotransmitters from the amygdala to the hypothalmus which sends a message to the pituitary gland which passes a hormone into the blood stream. Situated just above the kidneys, the adrenal gland detects the hormone and fires out adrenalin. This series of events, along what is referred to as the HPA axis, causes several things to happen very quickly. First, the noradrenalin in the brain accelerates the rate and volume of the heart and lungs and begins the chain reaction that leads to adrenalin being excreted by the kidneys. The adrenalin shuts down the digestive system, closes off blood supply to other parts of the body and diverts it instead to skeletal muscle by opening up the blood vessels there. By now symptoms are obvious; heavy breathing, a sinking feeling in the stomach, butterflies and sweaty palms. Climbers will be very aware of these and can often feel the effects either prior to or during a climb. Also the bladder relaxes. Have you ever needed a nervous wee before an route, exam or public speaking? Also peripheral vision shuts down in favour of sharper focus on threats or escape. Have you ever been so scared you become hold blind? Then shaking or jitteriness sets in as muscles anticipate explosive action.

Personally I have experienced all of these whilst climbing and I suspect that most climbers have. If you like, this is Muir's, *'life blazing forth'* but frankly the aptness of his phrase was not central to my thoughts when I was experiencing the symptoms. The label 'fight or flight', suggests readiness for two courses of action, both unsuitable when danger threatens on the mountain or rock face. The first is usually inappropriate and the second physically impossible unfortunately. But the good news is that these primal reflexes evolved because they increase our chances of survival. If we can keep them under control they enable us to perform beyond ourselves and to reach a level of performance that we were unaware we could possibly achieve.

The next wave of chemicals to be released in the body in response to fear is the endorphins. Serving a very important purpose, these closely resemble opiates although it is argued that the one most commonly produced in the body is 100 times more powerful than morphine. As well as pre-empting the need for pain relief in a fight or flight situation, they also create a feeling of well-being. Endorphins are released not only by fear. They also produce the high experienced after intense exercise, excitement, pain, love and orgasm. Descriptions of the sensation are very similar to those of the feelings of oneness frequently found in the climbing literature reviewed by Lester.

The final hormone to be released is dopamine. This provides an intrinsic 'feel good' reward to reinforce behaviour which works in any given situation. As explained in Chapter 1, this mechanism has evolved to reward curiosity so it is perhaps puzzling that dopamine is released when we are scared. But we are successful as a species because evolution has taught us first to recognise and then to deal with scary situations. Just as curiosity helped us explore the world around us, this fear based learning response dramatically increased our chances of survival. We curiously assess every situation we meet including its potential threats and our learned response may be anything from mild anxiety to pure terror. Body and mind are stimulated to react and, if successful and we survive, the size of the dopamine hit which is our reward is commensurate with the level of threat we have overcome.

That dopamine is essential to learn from the fear response has been shown by scientists using mice bred to be dopamine deficient. These were trained by being subjected to a loud noise at the same time as they received an electric shock in one foot. The dopamine deficient mice did not learn to associate the foot shock with the sound. But the control mice responded to the foot shock in the same way that they responded to the loud noise. The necessity of an immediate dose of dopamine was confirmed by injecting the deficient mice with dopamine immediately before or after the training. Then they too learned the response as successfully as the control group but the dopamine had no effect if the injection was delayed for an hour.

Clearly this is a form of the well known Pavlovian conditioning. Pavlov's dogs associated the ringing of a bell with food so strongly that the sound alone made them salivate. The dopamine mice show us the mechanism and the power of rewarding the fear response associated with stimuli like places and sounds. We humans are undeniably subject to the same process. We have all felt the results of our own conditioning; totally irresistible, it cannot be consciously overridden. When I was on the Llanberis Mountain Rescue Team, the call-outs were initiated by text. As soon as a message came I certainly experienced the same fear response I feel when I am climbing even when I was unable to go and knew I would not be attending.

Given the rapid and profound effects of the natural hormones, it is not surprising that drugs which stimulate their production or actually mimic them have been developed and have existed for a long time. It is also not surprising that the synthesized versions are strongly addictive. Amphetamine, the generic form of 'speed', for example produces a physiological response similar to that of noradrenalin; heightened awareness, increased heart rate and a feeling of being stronger and more energetic. The effect of cocaine is to release massive amounts of dopamine into the brain whilst simultaneously blocking its reuptake and that of other pleasure-associated neurotransmitters like serotonin.

Although it is disputed, it is strongly argued that addiction occurs through one of the routes dopamine takes through the brain, in particular the mesolimbic pathway that associates the drug with our intrinsic reward system. It is also argued that addiction to behaviour which triggers the reward system can happen in the same way. This is certainly supported by the fundamental law of psychology which states that any behaviour that is rewarded will be strengthened.

The addictive effect of dopamine rewarding risk taking recently emerged from a treatment for Parkinson's Disease. Caused by the death of dopamine producing cells in the brain, the disease affects the central nervous system producing movement problems and tremors. Early treatment is to administer a drug which stops the declining supply of the hormone being metabolised away. To begin with dopamine levels are raised and an observed side effect in a few cases has been pathological gambling. The added reward provided by dopamine has turned some otherwise ordinary people into compulsive gamblers.

One case study[117] provides a dramatic illustration. A 52 year old married man being treated for Parkinson's Disease

---

117 Pathological Gambling Caused by Drugs Used to Treat Parkinson Disease -

http://archneur.jamanetwork.com/article.aspx?articleid=789393

decided to increase his own dose, presumably to increase its stabilising effect. Before that, he gambled only occasionally and had never lost more than $400. After taking the drug, his gambling became uncontrollable and he lost more than $100 000. He gained 50lb in weight through compulsive eating and became obsessed with sex and pornography, engaging in several extramarital affairs. After his medication was reduced and the dopamine levels dropped those problems vanished.

Clearly, all three of the hormones released by fear have possible addictive qualities. As we can see, the association of reward with fear, a mechanism fine tuned by evolution to keep us safe, could have the ironic consequence of making some of us addicted to scary situations. Could this be a sufficient explanation for increased participation in extreme sports and does it account for why some people describe themselves as 'hooked' on their favourite activities? Dr Michael Davis, a neuroscientist at Emory University, said that, whilst..............

"..........there haven't been studies on so-called action sports, (but) the general scientific thinking is that the more fearful a certain sport makes you, the greater the release of these chemicals. The greater the release of the chemicals, the greater the addiction-like symptoms".[118]

So an addiction to risk or fear has never been proven in sport but Davis implies that this is only because the research has yet to be done. By logical extension then, it must be alarming for sporting risk takers that, as with many addictive drugs, a tolerance soon builds up and the addict needs a bigger dose to get the same effect. In the case of climbing, would this mean being scared more often? Or being more scared by being in greater danger? Whether sustaining the same feeling would equate to

---

118 http://www.psychologytoday.com/blog/the-playing-field/200803/the-addicitve-nature-adrenaline-sport

climbing harder, bolder or more often it is hard to say. Maybe the average recreational climber never reaches a level of participation which develops risk- or fear-addiction. Possibly the research is better applied to elite climbers who participate far more often. Marvin Zuckerman, whose research features later on, says in an email that......

"......*the* [Everest and other extreme] *expedition and elite mountain climbers are among the highest* [scorers on the Sensation Seeking scale], *not only on the subscale Thrill and Adventure Seeking but also on the more general Experience Seeking subscale*".

That is to say that they scored higher on those scales than participants in any other risk based sport[119].

I offer as anecdotal evidence observations of two people I have known for a long time who excel in climbing at the most elite level; Leo Houlding and Tim Emmett. Both seem to feel compelled steadily to increase the difficulty and riskiness of the type of activity they have been doing over the last fifteen years. Leo was already one of the greatest 'trad' climbers in the UK and has since become one of the few to have taken that free climbing skill to big walls. He did so first on the reasonably comfortable surroundings of El Capitan in Yosemite and then in more remote and adventurous locations like Baffin Island, the Venezuelan rainforest and Antarctica.

Both Tim and Leo have gone on virtually to invent a new sub-sport of climbing so extreme that the number engaged in it globally can be counted on one hand. Para-alpinism is the combination of climbing huge alpine walls and BASE jumping off the top. Having climbed an extreme route, Leo, Tim and a select group of others will, if the conditions are right, jump off the cliff in the most

---

119 Sensation Seeking and Risky Behavior – M. Zuckerman 2007.

extreme form of parachuting.

Another way of testing the addiction-to-fear hypothesis might be to see if there are withdrawal symptoms when the cause of the fear, in this case climbing, becomes unavailable. Although there are no studies on climbing or other risk based sports, there is literature on the psychological effects of injury to sportsmen and women. Whilst not necessarily regularly exposed to the same intense fear response as climbers, they do experience the anxiety and thrill of competition and some similar hormonal responses to hard training. A study in 1992 found injured athletes were.....

"......*statistically more tense, hostile, depressed, unsure, tired and confused than their non-injured peers.*"[20]

The symptoms of withdrawal from cocaine include depression, anxiousness, irritability, fatigue, tiredness and agitation. The two lists are remarkably similar. This is inconclusive of course but an interesting route for possible future studies.

Personally I have had several injuries which caused me to stop climbing for prolonged periods and have felt effects similar to those withdrawal symptoms. The wait for a prolapsed disc of cartilage in my back to heal affected me so deeply I was diagnosed with the depression I have battled with ever since. Many climbing friends report feeling down when recovering from injuries and many look for solace by taking up other risk based sports. Climbers and mountaineers often describe post expedition blues as if they experience a 'come down' or 'withdrawal period' after prolonged excitement. Admittedly, this is further anecdotal evidence. But reports are so frequent and

120 Emotional Effects of Sports Injuries: Implications for Physiotherapists -

http://www.sciencedirect.com/science/article/pii/S0031940610616422

so widespread this alone gives a degree of validity until science quantifies the physical effects of being deprived of the risk some of us seek. The commonly experienced negative moods described here will also help us later to examine how risk takers define themselves and use risk to provide the escape they sometimes need.

In summary, whether or not people become addicted to the kind of risk encountered in extreme sports where the outcome could be physical injury or death has yet to be scientifically proven. It must also be emphasised that the research reviewed here does not actually link risk taking in sport with addiction. But the evidence I have cited from related fields indicates that addiction to risk taking in sport is a far broader issue than the use of the pejorative term 'adrenaline junkie' would imply.

The possibility that some of us could be more predisposed than others to develop an addiction to risk taking and that this could be an inherited trait adds a further layer of complexity. It has long been recognised that some people become addicted to the kind of risk taking provided by commercial gambling. Some current studies are examining whether the predisposition to become a compulsive gambler is determined by DNA and, if it exists, whether the gene can be passed on.

This research is in its early days because until recently not enough was known about the human genetic code. In fact, 13 years of collaborative research worldwide were needed to map the 3.2 billion base pairs of genetic code in the human genome, work which was completed in 2003. Early technology could map only 300 to 800 base pairs a day but now the Beijing Genomic Institute has 128 of the latest Illumina sequencers which allow the equivalent of 1000 human genomes to be mapped every day. Like the early computer engineers who suffered the 'tyranny of numbers', geneticists struggle with these vast amounts of data. But researchers can now map areas of the human genome to identified brain functions to find out whether particular behaviours are predetermined by DNA. This offspring of bio-psychology is called behavioural genetics.

No sooner had the new science come into being than those connections began to be found. At first, researchers were intent on mapping each clearly identifiable behaviour to a single piece of genetic code that had been traced to a specific brain function. Early on, risk-taking became one subject of the research because many forms of it are anti-social; obsessive gambling, drug taking, alcohol addiction and dangerous driving amongst others.

Key in this research is that part of DNA which has been mapped to the development of dopamine receptors. Without these, dopamine could not stimulate the pleasurable euphoria which is the reward in our reward system. The responsible part of our genetic code, the DRD4 gene, can be repeated anything from 2 to 11 times with the most common number of repeats being 4. Some studies link more repeats with more risk-taking whilst others show no relation. The likelihood of the number of repeats being a risk-taking indicator is currently 60-40 in favour. This is hardly conclusive but a limitation of all these studies is that they placed people into a high- or a low-dopamine receptor group with the low group having less than 7 repeats and the high group having 7 or more. Conventional psychological research predicts clearer results if three groups were used; a low group of below 4 and a high group of above 8 with the middle group being disregarded. Research findings are also difficult to interpret because different studies have not used the same measures of risk and sensation-seeking which may well have introduced inconsistency. It also seems that the assumption that a specific behaviour is determined by a single gene is unlikely to provide useful answers.

Another of the genes identified as being potentially linked to risk taking behaviour has been given the media-friendly name *Warrior Gene*. It might however more accurately be called the *Psychopath Gene* because it has been linked to psychopaths, both those who function successfully in society and those non-functioning psychopaths who are usually diagnosed as clinically insane. The research which led to the discovery of this gene attracted much publicity and controversy[121]. It all started in Holland where a woman was so concerned about a trait shown by the male side of her family that she went to a doctor for help. Tracing back the family tree revealed the full extent of the problem. Since the 1870s, males in her family had all had serious learning difficulties and had exhibited extremely aggressive behaviour that was anti-social to the point of criminality. Their crimes included rape, violent assault and arson.

In one of the earliest pieces of research into human genetics, a mutation in their DNA was eventually isolated that effectively stopped the production of monoamine oxidase. This enzyme regulates the level of serotonin, a brain chemical that has a calming effect amongst other functions. Put simply, if dopamine is the go signal for behaviour then serotonin is the stop mechanism. With a serious serotonin deficiency, the males in the unfortunate woman's family went from mild irritation to uncontrollable rage with very little provocation and terrifyingly quickly.

Researchers subsequently looked for different versions

---

121 Born To Rage: A Case Study of the Warrior Gene - An overview of controversy surrounding the warrior gene -

http://wakespace.lib.wfu.edu/xmlui/bitstream/handle/10339/37295/Murphy_wfu_0248M_10224.pdf?sequence=1 of the mutated gene in other subjects and found high and low versions. The low version has been linked to more aggressive behaviour so it acquired the name *Warrior Gene* and it is now possible to be tested for it by a private company for the bargain price of $99. This is almost certainly a rip off since the colourful term is a simplistic misnomer. Perhaps those with the gene struggle to control a tendency to anti-social behaviour but it turns out that it can also give them attributes considered to be desirable. What tips the balance seems to be not genetics but upbringing, itself probably the most powerful conditioning process there is of course.

The reputation of the *Warrior Gene* for causing criminally psychopathic behaviour helped a convicted murderer to get his sentence reduced from the electric chair to life. In the US in 2009, Brad Waldroup pleaded guilty on the grounds of diminished responsibility because of his genes and his upbringing. It had already been established that those with the *Warrior Gene* who have a conventional, ordered childhood exhibit only socially acceptable psychopathic traits and manage to stay within the Law. However, those with the gene who have a chaotic or abusive upbringing are much more predisposed to become violent criminals. Of the convicted criminals invited to take part in the study because they had the *Warrior Gene*, many exhibited psychopathic behaviour and many had been abused as children. This was explained as the means by which their resilience to non-functioning psychotic behaviour was lowered to the point where they did not learn to discern right from wrong. An interesting aside is that one of the behaviours psychologists use to define psychopathy is thrill seeking.

Another piece of research in the US confirmed that some psychopathic behaviours are socially acceptable. Business leaders in this study displayed on average four times more psychopathic tendencies than the normal population. Clearly the line between the high achiever and the clinically insane can be a perilously fine one. In more recent research, low levels of the *Warrior Gene* have been linked with being more than usually able to make decisions and take financial risks[122]. The lack of the controlling brake serotonin seems to help some people to distance their emotions when making decisions. However, when decision makers lack the ability to discern right and wrong then the outcomes will be amoral and possibly socially unacceptable as demonstrated by subjects who were willing to increase retribution when provoked in laboratory experiments[123]. A finding particularly relevant to risk taking is that people with low levels of the MAO gene may be more likely to make decisions impulsively.

The enzyme that the *Warrior Gene* affects comes in two forms, an A and a B type and there have been non-genetic studies into both which found that the B type deals with dopamine and is related to sensation seeking. Low levels of MAO-B have been linked to high measures of sensation seeking in a majority of studies[124] and research into a wide range of conditions regarded either as addictions or diseases. These include; attention deficit hyperactivity disorder, antisocial personality disorder, long term criminality, alcoholism, drug abuse, pathological gambling and paranoid schizophrenia.

As with research into psychopathic behaviour, all the

122

http://rspb.royalsocietypublishing.org/content/278/1714/2053.short

123 http://www.pnas.org/content/106/7/2118.short

124 Personality and Risk Taking by Zuckerman & Kuhlman -

http://grupsderecerca.uab.cat/zkpq/sites/grupsderecerca.uab.cat.zkpq/f iles/zkpq8.pdf studies attempt to disentangle the effects of their subjects' genetic legacy from those of their upbringing. The perennial 'nature versus nurture' issue has been tackled particularly successfully in studies of twins who were genetically identical but, because they were separated at birth by adoption, had been brought up differently. The tests focused on the trait of sensation seeking which has been shown to be associated with risk taking generally and in sport[125]. The conclusion was that the trait is inherited in up to 50% of cases. In other research looking at determinants of personality, non-identical twins who had shared the same upbringing as identical twin siblings took part. Again it was found that up to 50% of personality traits could be ascribed to their genes. If this is confirmed by follow-up studies, then the inescapable conclusion has to be that up to half of an individual's personality is genetically predetermined.

So, since genetic makeup is linked both to a tendency to take risks and to personality traits, then a connection between a particular type of personality and a desire to take risks should be apparent. And indeed, this has been shown to exist but is less than clear because personality measures have been altered over the years. Marvin Zuckerman, a leading researcher into risk cited earlier, has extended his Sensation Seeking scale to produce the Zuckerman-Kulhman Five Factor Personality Questionnaire to quantify traits which he linked to risk-taking. However this is aligned too closely to risk takers to be generally useful as a personality test. It was when a more universally applicable test was devised and the 'Big Five' aspects of personality were widely accepted that arguably more consistently standardised research was possible. More than one version exists so I refer only to the open source International Personality Item Pool which

---

125 Marvin Zuckerman – Sensation Seeking and Risky Behavior - 2007

uses the 'Big Five' personality traits; Extraversion, Agreeableness, Conscientiousness, Emotional Stability and Openness to Experience.

Extraversion, Emotional Stability and a lack of Conscientiousness had each been shown separately to affect risk taking and clearly some combination of those three was involved. To deal with the problems encountered when a single trait was tested in relation to a single behaviour, Castanier, le Scanff and Woodman[126] used multiple personality traits to make a multidimensional model. To achieve this they grouped individual subjects previously linked to risk taking into high and low scorers. Then they selected people with particular combinations of traits from those groups. Those with low Conscientiousness and either high Extraversion or high Neuroticism were found to be more inclined to engage in risky behaviour; high risk personalities. Conversely, they also found those considered to have a low risk personality type to score at the opposite ends of those scales; high for Conscientiousness with either low Extraversion or low Neuroticism. The three types of high risk personality were described as people who would be Impulsive, Hedonistic or Insecure. The Impulsive and Hedonistic people respectively fitted neatly into psychotic and risk-addicted models of behaviour. But that left the Insecure and it was argued that they fitted into a group who take risks to satisfy an emotional need.

That risk taking fulfils an emotional need is surely intuitively accepted by most climbers. Lester's literature review certainly found it expressed in many ways in accounts of the personal experiences of climbers and

---

126 Who Takes Risks in High Risk Sports? A Typological Personality Approach, Castanier, C. Le Scanff, C. & Woodman, T. Research Quarterly for Exercise and Sport, Vol 81, 2010.

mountaineers. As we saw earlier, he separated these into eight themes no less than five of which provide labels for different emotional responses; *Contact with a Better Self, Assertion of Self, Conquest of Self, Escape from Self* and *Unity.* Definitions are provided by the following extracts from climbers' accounts;

Contact with a Better Self occurs when one feels purer, more honestly and more authentically oneself. Lionel Terray was on the epic ascent of Annapurna with Maurice Herzog and in his book, aptly entitled *"The Borders of the Impossible",* he says,

"I began to realize that the mountain is no more than an indifferent wasteland of rock and ice with no other value than what we choose to give it, but that on this infinitely virgin material each man could mould, by the creative force of the spirit, the form of his own ideal."

Escape from Self suggests that sufficient challenge can give one an escape from a deeper feeling of discomfort or a release from life's more mundane aspects. Reinhold Messner recalls,

"Each movement was neither work nor action, merely being. And being was freedom. And freedom was older than time."

Assertion of Self reflects the feeling one has sometimes when climbing of being the principal agent in one's own life, no longer a pawn controlled by someone else or as Frank Smythe put it,

"...to rise superior to his environment is the great privilege of man".
Messner felt......
".....to be alone and trusting only to my abilities gave me a strong feeling of identity".

The Conquest of Self refers to the development and testing of self-control and self-discipline. Mark Twight in his *"Extreme Alpinism"*, a kind of how to remove your brain and succeed in spite of the mental and physical difficulties of high-end modern alpinism, says,

"You can only let go, allowing instinctual reaction to prevail instead of conscious reaction, if you believe 100% in the ability of the unconscious to direct the action".

Lester's final theme was the *Unity* expressed by individual climbers who feel 'completely and wholly' themselves when engaged in the mountains, as if in 'real life' they felt constrained to be what society wanted them to be.

The need that many people, including climbers, seem to have to see themselves in the best light or to escape something in themselves has been examined by Taylor and Hamilton[127]. They explored two possible motives for sensation seeking; escape and compensation. The origins of their work go back to 1981 when a theory of emotional self-regulation through self-awareness began to be developed. The theory proposed that as individuals we choose to focus either on ourselves and in the process become self-aware or we focus on the external world to avoid self-awareness.

In becoming self-aware we can carry out important psychological functions but in the process become goal orientated in our behaviour. The goals are not necessarily set deliberately or consciously, they can be set sub-consciously. Then the more we focus on ourselves, the more we notice discrepancies between our goals and our present state. When the difference between an ideal self (where we would like to be) and a real self (where we

---

127 Taylor and Hamilton. Preliminary Evidence for the role of self-regulatory processes in sensation seeking. Anxiety, Stress and Coping, 1997.

actually are) is a gap too far to bridge, there is a negative effect. If we cannot see a way to reach our goal, we either stop trying to attain it or we simply turn our attentions elsewhere.

To illustrate this with a scenario familiar to many climbers, we set ourselves goals which are arranged sub-consciously in an ordered fashion and going to the wall to train, for example, would be just a part of the goal to climb harder. This in turn might be part of a goal to climb to a particular grade that is part of a bigger plan to climb a dream route. Then if training goes badly or we cannot see how what we are doing now will help us to reach any of our goals, we are likely to switch to another activity which is sure to bring success. As a result, we are far more likely to train our strengths than our weaknesses or we may refocus on a totally different aspect of our life.

The example Taylor and Hamilton use is the student who finds difficulty in one subject and probably focuses his effort on another subject because thinking about the problems of reaching the original goal is negative and we prefer to think positively. Similarly, I am sure many of us find ourselves engaged in pointless activities as the deadline for some work we are struggling with looms closer. The 'displacement activities', as they are known, replace the hard stuff with things that are easier to achieve. When we cannot achieve a goal and be our 'ideal self', we re-focus our attention and accept a version who achieves easier things but at least this self has got something done and is not a complete failure.

There is a raft of psychological literature on behaviour patterns which involve how we regulate which version of 'self' to apply in different situations. In any given set of circumstances, we have an 'ideal self' as a model and an 'actual self' including many versions of our social 'self'.

Some research concludes that having several versions of 'self' is good because, if we become distressed with one of our forms of self, we can focus on another especially if those roles are easily assumed and discarded. With this flexibility, we can avoid challenges that are unrewarding and difficult by resorting to rewarding and less difficult ones.

How we regulate or move between different versions of 'self' is key. If there is a problem in our self-regulation we have two options; either stop being self aware by switching attention to something external or assume another self which gives a greater feeling of self worth. Those who have fewer forms of self can suffer higher levels of depression and anxiety because they have fewer goals to choose from and often over-value those they have as a result. Essentially, if they find they have no way of increasing their self worth, they become depressed or anxious as they are forced through lack of positive outlets to focus on the negative or they try to escape those feelings by shifting to an external focus such as rock climbing.

We need next to look at self regulation in the context of risk taking. There are   kinds of risk that are usually premeditated like climbing which require training and preparation. There are other risky activities like drinking, drug-taking or driving recklessly that are more spur of the moment than planned. Of course, the opposite can often be true; climbers do make snap decisions to try routes whereas drug and alcohol abusers sometimes plan binges. I could give many examples of both types of decision from my own climbing career.

The ascent of *Right Wall* mentioned earlier in the book, definitely falls into the premeditated category. I had trained for a long period before finally climbing it. Very much an impulsive decision, on the other hand, was the first ascent of a new route on the *Dervish Slab* in the Slate Quarries above my home village of Llanberis. I did top-rope it successfully once 6 months previously but I had done very little climbing since and certainly nothing of the grade this route turned out to be. Heading out that day, I had planned on doing only the two classics on the slab, *Last Tango in Paris* and *Comes the Dervish*. Having climbed both of them hundreds of times, I felt I was just going through the motions. On a sudden impulse, I chose to attempt this technically thin and extremely bold new line. I arranged some gear, returned to the ground, tried to centre myself and intoned a little mantra, "Just keep going", "Just keep going." As I set off again I quickly reached a point of no return. Utterly committed, those words "Just keep going" overcame all other thoughts and, emerging from the other side with the route in the bag, I was freed from worldly burdens. It was me and the rock. An incredibly rewarding experience, I had not prepared or trained for it. It had happened purely because of a decision made with very little thought that day. Maybe there is a darker side to my personal risk taking behaviour or maybe my fear based associative learning kicked in and I was just trying to get a natural high?

Imagine a simple binary world where all decisions are either planned and prepared for or made on the spur of the moment and we will examine how each arises when we are taking risks. A planned risk gives us another self with which to carry out self regulation. In that situation, we make the decision to give ourselves a new opportunity to maintain self-worth or a particular self-image. There are no links to negative aspects with this form of functional risk taking and Taylor and Hamilton coined the term the Compensation Motive for the reasons why some of us actively seek other avenues of personal identity. 'Compensators' have a sense of accomplishment. As a result, they will feel good about themselves, will be more likely to plan ahead and will link the act of risk taking with their self image.

In contrast, the reason for making a sudden decision to risk it all, as I did in the Quarries that day, is to avoid self-awareness and is labelled the Escape Motive by Taylor and Hamilton. In general, 'Escapees' were found to be more likely to have higher anxiety levels, negative moods and depression. Using the Risk and Excitement Inventory they created as their psychometric research tool, Taylor and Hamilton concluded that Escapees show a narrowing of attention. They are more likely to act spontaneously and focus on the physical sensations of their activity rather than the emotions it evokes. This fits observations that a risk taker forced, by injury maybe, to take fewer risks may feel something akin to withdrawal symptoms and experience negative moods. Similarly, someone who already suffers negative moods may take up climbing for the very reason that it helps alleviate those feelings. In this 'chicken and egg' situation, cause and effect cannot be disentangled and are arguably interchangeable.

We need to look deeper because when we make a real life decision our motives are rarely polarised like this. Usually we adopt a role which is partly Compensator and partly Escapee. The extent to which we are one or the other at a given time for a particular purpose depends on a complex mix of factors and influences.

The far reaching study[128] by Cazenave, le Scanff and Woodman I describe next investigated this mix by examining the psychological profiles of risk takers using

---

128 Psychological profiles and emotional regulation characteristics of women engaged in risk-taking sports, N. Cazenave, C Le Scanff and Tim Woodman. Anxiety, Stress and Coping 2007.

the Risk and Excitement Inventory and the Sensation Seeking Scale. But it also used measures of impulsiveness and the extent to which the subjects were affected by their emotions. Clearly, gender bias needed to be eliminated so the subjects were exclusively female and were selected from three comparative groups;

non-risk takers (the control group) - swimmers, dancers, table tennis players, golfers and athletes

risk takers in sports for leisure purposes - mountaineers, BASE jumpers, parachute jumpers, downhill skiers, snowboarders and downhill mountain bikers

risk takers in sports for professional reasons - mountain guides, rally drivers, sky divers, downhill skiers and snowboarders

The indicator used by the researchers to gauge the importance of emotion in the decision making of their subjects was whether or not they had the condition alexithymia. This condition is defined by the Diagnostic and Statistical Manual of Mental Disorder[129] as either the inability to feel emotions or express emotions, or both of these.

I digress here because I find it interesting that alexithymia, together with impulsiveness, sounds very like the result produced by the psychopathy gene although I should stress that this was not a focus of the research. The effect on behaviour of a total lack of emotion is illustrated rather alarmingly in the following extract from Kent Keihl's interview with Brian Dugan. Serving a double life sentence for rape and murder, Dugan scored in the 99th percentile of the psychopath test and he said..........

---

129 This is the manual that American Psychiatric Association publishes to describe and classify mental disorders. Alexithymia was only classified in the latest 2012 fifth edition of the Manual.

"I have empathy, too – but it's like it just stops. I mean, I start to feel, but something just blocks it. I don't know what it is."[130]

Trying to explain his crime, Dugan said in an emotionless voice,

"She came to the door and ... I clicked, I turned into Mr. Hyde from Dr. Jekyll."

Kent Keihl highlighted the problem...........

"What if I told you that a psychopath has an emotional IQ that's like a 5-year-old?"

Returning to the main findings of the research, it would be natural to expect that the main differences would be between the psychological profiles of the risk takers and those of the non-risk takers. But this was not borne out. Instead, the most striking differences proved to be between the risk takers for leisure purposes and the rest; both the professional risk takers and the control group of non-risk takers.

The leisure risk takers came out ahead of the other two groups in all tests. They were more impulsive and more likely to be sensation seeking. They were more likely to be Escapees on the Risk and Excitement Scale from which we can infer that they therefore probably suffered more of the associated negative effects; increased anxiety, depression and low self worth. When alexithymia was considered as a possible reason for their need to escape, it turned out that indeed, they scored higher than the other groups showing either that they felt their emotions less acutely or that they expressed them less ably than the professionals and the non-risk takers.

The differences between the professional risk takers

---

130 Barbara Hagerty – Inside a Psychopath's Brain: The Sentencing Debate –

http://www.npr.org/templates/story/story.php?storyId=128116806

and the non-risk takers (the control group) were far less dramatic. The professionals proved to be the least impulsive group of all but they were slightly more sensation seeking than the control group. The Risk and Excitement Inventory showed both groups to be Compensators implying that the professionals' risk taking provided them with ways of boosting self worth and positive self-awareness. Surprisingly, the professionals scored lower than the non-risk takers on the alexithymia scale so they were the most likely of the three groups to engage their emotions when making their decisions.

These findings beg the question; why are the motives of the person engaged in risk taking as a professional different from those of recreational risk takers? Cazenave, le Scanff and Woodman hypothesised that the main difference between the two groups itself provides the reason. They argued that the two distinct psychological types self-regulated in different ways so that.......
'..............*women who deliberately take risks as part of their leisure activities (without training and supervisory staff, and even, sometimes without many of the requisite skills) will have a more negative psychological profile than women who have a profession that is based on risk-taking. Indeed professional risk-takers have acquired a social acknowledgement and recognition in their professional (risk-taking) field.*'

I would challenge the reasons behind that hypothesis. Working as I do as a professional mountaineering instructor alongside many colleagues, I know that we all began as recreational risk takers and we fitted the profile of the study's leisure group fairly closely. As we gained experience and sought qualifications we migrated to the professional group. The research does not address the movement from amateur to professional and it is important since every professional risk taker in the study must have made that switch at some point. None contradicted the gloomy predictions of careers teachers by starting a job as a rally driver or a sky diver the week after leaving school. Their career paths all began with lengthy periods as amateurs. To my mind, what separated the professional subjects from the leisure group was essentially time and experience.

Self evidently, not everyone who engages in risky leisure pursuits, however skilled or talented, chooses to become professional. Amongst any leisure risk takers, it seems likely that psychological differences would distinguish those suited to a professional career from the rest. So the differences displayed by the professional research subjects may have been apparent at an early stage and could perhaps be regarded as intrinsic. On the other hand, could they have been acquired over time through training and experience?

The research does not acknowledge the personal attributes needed by many professionals, having the patience to look after novices for example. The criterion for selecting professional risk takers for the study was that they all made a living from their sports. No distinction was made between roles represented by instructors, guides and elite sponsored sportswomen amongst others, each requiring attributes which might affect a psychological profile. The professional group was also on average more than 10 years older than the leisure group so facets of personality which change with age may have contributed to the differences found.

I think that the addiction hypothesis should be cautiously reconsidered here as well. I imagine that the recreational risk takers could not engage in risky activities as often as if they had no other commitments so their psychological profiles may have reflected the negative effect of withdrawal. In my experience, the professionals' risk taking would be closely related to their precise role. Instructors and guides spend their time at work with clients and students diligently controlling risk. But in their free time, with their chosen sport providing as much risk as they wish, some of their decisions will be planned and others will be made on impulse. In contrast, elite sports people, especially those who compete, seem to maximise the risks they take when they perform.

I am speculating here on areas outside the remit of the research but I offer the sheer complexity of the activities of the professional risk takers as the reason why their profiles are less distinct from those of the control group and why their motives are so difficult to interpret. Because of its simplicity, it is hard to disagree with the above statement from the researchers that professionals have a variety of ways to nurture their self worth and are therefore less likely to suffer the negative effects of escapism. But we do not yet have the full story about why some of us consider the kinds of risk others regard as foolhardy to be an essential part of our lives.

In this chapter I set myself the task of finding out why climbers climb. I did warn you at the beginning that this question and the more general 'why do risk takers take risks?' has been the subject of much speculation, theorising and research for decades. As promised, condensing vast swathes of current thinking in psychology, neuroscience and genetics has not been straight forward and has produced many possibilities. On the plus side, these are all more enlightening than poor old Mallory's 'because it's there' and amongst them must be The Answer.

It cannot be denied that the popular view that risk takers become addicted to the   buzz they get when they scare themselves is very plausible. Apparently resembling the   quasi-religious   euphoria   described   by   many mountaineers and climbers, the aftermath of the body's 'fight or flight' response feels like a natural high which lots of us seem to need to the point that we feel down when we are deprived of a regular dose. The same hormonal pathway and reward system are responsible for drug addiction, alcoholism and compulsive behaviour too. So far, so convincing but the existence of the adrenaline junkie has not actually been established beyond doubt in a sporting context.

Genetic inheritance is a strong contender of course. In spite of some contradictory evidence, how could it not be? Parts of the human genome definitely determine the likelihood that we will behave in particular ways. Work is in the early stages but already we know that sometimes the affect is as direct as control of mechanisms which produce mood shifting hormones. But our genes shape, at most, only half of our personality it seems. That leaves a great deal to be moulded and conditioned by other influences and factors. In the future, the science of behavioural genetics will continue to reveal which of our attributes we have inherited, bringing benefits even greater than understanding why climbers climb, as long as we guard against its use as a eugenic tool.

Significant results have been produced by conventional psychological research into the types of personalities who take risks. The need to take risks changes with age and there are gender differences too but the Hedonistic, Impulsive and Insecure amongst us are more likely to engage in risky activities. Some of us naturally engage our emotions more in the decisions we make when taking risks and those of us who do not, may be psychotic but in a nice way.

Perhaps the most promising research I have reviewed looks at the emotional function of risk taking as a benefit we gain from our sports. This was actually carried out in a sporting setting and is directly applicable. It shows that many of us use our risk taking to regulate our emotions and provide positive versions of self. It shows that risk based activities can provide us with an escape from ourselves and everyday life or alternatively with a means to develop self awareness and self worth. At the very least, this valuably points us at something we can learn to control and change.

All the research considered here grouped people according to variables, found a mean value for each group and looked for statistically significant differences between them. Average trends emerged like snapshots which, whilst informative, were hazy at best. If you are a climber, if you peer into the snapshots, you may recognise some aspects of your personality and some of the reasons why you climb. As a unique individual, you cannot find yourself pictured more accurately than that. Hopefully though, you will also have gained some insight into why other climbers climb too. And that is The Answer or at least as good an approximation as can be given for now.

We climb essentially for enjoyment, regardless of where that enjoyment comes from. That to me is the most important aspect of why I climb. I head out to challenge myself against gravity by rock climbing and if it was not fun then I would probably have given up years ago. The same is undoubtedly true of all the pioneers who have come before us and all of those who will follow in their footsteps. We all head to the heights to put smiles on our faces.

8 INDOOR CLIMBING, TRAINING AND THE FUTURE

If the increase in climbing participation seemed dramatic throughout the 60s and 70s, then growth over the last twenty years has been explosive by comparison. That has been partly because of the growing commercialisation and media attention attracted by the sport during that period but also because of radical changes in outdoor education. Today an entire industry has grown up to provide qualified and experienced instructors to meet that demand and to satisfy the requirement for all British school children to experience learning outside the classroom. These factors steadily swelled the numbers engaged in climbing outdoors way beyond previous expectations but what produced a truly exponential increase was the appearance of the climbing wall.

Allowing city dwellers to practice in the middle of their working week and all year round regardless of the weather sent the number of climbers into orbit. So we shall explore the importance of the rise of indoor climbing along with the belief which brought it about; that as in any sport, rock climbing skills should be specifically and systematically developed and trained. There was a time when this was a strange, and to some an almost heretical, concept. But the early converts pushed climbing into the realms of what had once seemed physically impossible and unthinkably bold and daring. These climbers forced the next wave of progress and their influence proved irresistible. Those who tried to emulate them went looking for training facilities too but they also sought the latest innovations in technology and used them to great effect. This is still true now of course in our digital age. Computers affect our lives and our climbing in ways that could never have been foreseen then and this chapter would not be complete without an attempt to predict what may be possible in the future

A look at the evidence of the first signs of a move towards training and the use of climbing walls shows that both were happening a surprisingly long time ago. In fact, the history of indoor climbing goes back further than you might expect. Since long before the appearance of the purpose built indoor wall, bridges, buildings and any structure that offered hand and footholds were used as year round practice facilities. But focussed training itself predates climbing walls by many years. Rock climbing as a sport developed well over a century ago as mountaineers determined to achieve harder, more technical mountain routes looked for training opportunities on steep crags. Much later still, dedicated rock climbers themselves turned to bouldering and eventually to indoor climbing in preparation for pushing their grades.

It is true that advances in equipment made attempts on steeper, harder terrain safer but the application of training to climbing was undoubtedly the key to the rise in standards. The roots of specific training can be traced as far back as the late 1800s. By then climbers were already climbing on the steep sides of boulders to improve their strength and expertise safely with increasingly difficult moves close to the ground before testing themselves high on a cliff. At that time Haskett-Smith was ridiculing early 'boulderers' in the Lake District but Aleister Crowley ran a bouldering competition in the Himalaya in 1893 and Oscar Eckenstein , his climbing partner, held balanced climbing workshops on some boulders near Pen y Pass in North Wales. The bouldering comp and the climbing coach are not the modern phenomena some of us thought then. Eckenstein seems to have excelled at bouldering and Crowley said of him at Wasdale.....

"There is a climb on the east face of the Y-Shaped boulder...

near Wastdale [sic] *Head Hotel which he was the only man to do, though many quite first-rate climbers tried it."*

It is only recently and thanks to research completed by Clint Warren[131] for a historical perspective on Lakeland climbing that this came to light. In the old hotel guest books he found not only a reference to the Y Boulder, but a topo and guide to the problems.

As early as 1878, French mountaineers were working hard on the boulders of Fontainebleau in preparation for the Alps. But it was probably not until the 1930s that this simple pastime began to be regarded as worthwhile in its own right. At that time, Pierre Allain, whose skills had been honed on 'Font' boulder problems and tested on many first ascents in the Alps, created the first purpose made rock shoe. Suitably equipped and completely dedicated, he and his companions in the forest produced a dramatic rise in the level of difficulty they consistently achieved. Some of their problems from that period would have had a grade equivalent to V3 or English 6a/b. Modern climbers will realise that this grade is astonishing for the time and it was several years before it was beaten.

The next breakthrough in trained performance is popularly attributed to John Gill who began rock climbing in 1953 and took up gymnastics and bodyweight exercise[132] in 1954. Although he was responsible for pioneering new boulder problems and moves of up to V9, his bodyweight exercises have made him the legend he is in bouldering

---

131 This comes from the fascinating history of bouldering on John Gill's website which is updated when new and interesting historical evidence emerges. http://johngill.net

132 Bodyweight exercises are generally exercises without the use of weights. John Gill was a master of a variety of exercises that utilised variations on the pull up.

and training for climbing. Photographs of him doing pull ups on a single finger and of his one arm front lever with his perfectly horizontal body suspended by one hand from a bar still astound people today. One feat that is hidden in the depths of his website left me in shock too; a front lever suspended from only the middle finger of his right hand! This pioneer regarded climbing as an extension of gymnastics and bouldering as a sport in its own right and not simply a preparation for roped climbing. His bodyweight exercises were undoubtedly the foundation for his bouldering achievements and an inspiration for many since.

In the UK, people did not immediately accept the usefulness of specific training for climbing other than climbing itself of course and there was plenty of that going on. Those taking up the sport in the fifties and their role models fitted their climbing around their working week and had precious little time for extra training on top. Also the widespread gym facilities we take for granted now and the growing fitness culture which has produced them did not exist. So it must have taken a huge leap of faith and imagination on the part of Don Robinson[133], a lecturer in physical education, to build the first indoor climbing wall in 1964. This occupied a single corridor of Leeds University and was little more than a modified brick wall with some edges and stonework inserted to create holds.

Four years later, John Syrett arrived at the university. A virtual novice to climbing, he trained on the wall with a fanatical obsession. Although he had little outdoor experience, he burst dramatically onto the British climbing

---

133 This section on the early climbing walls and training comes from a Mick Ward Article on UKClimbing.com called, 'Wall Warriors! A history of training for climbing'.

http://www.ukclimbing.com/articles/page.php?id=3398

scene in the summer of 1970, repeating many of the hardest routes, often solo. In particular, his repeat of an E3 6a on Yorkshire grit stone, *Wall of Horrors,* drew a short response from the climbing community, *'training on the Leeds wall'*. Through his training, Syrett had become one of the best climbers of his day and the significance of this is best captured in the words of experienced climbing coach Mick Ward,

"Because of one climber on one route, Leeds wall became sexy. Because Leeds wall became sexy, climbing walls became sexy. Today, 40 years later, there are thousands of climbing walls, all over the world."

Like John Gill, Syrett was an accomplished gymnast, who brought flexibility and power to his climbing along with the focus to train specifically for routes. He went on to make around 40 first ascents on grit stone and to free climb sections of many other existing routes previously thought to be possible only with aid. His route *The Big Greenie,* a short fingery wall at Almscliffe, was described by Jim Perrin as,

".... one of the most significant outcrop routes in a post-Brown era".

Even more remarkable than Syrett's own achievements was the huge influence he had on his sport. He inspired his contemporaries by showing what was within their grasp with dedicated training and unleashed the 'gold rush' of hard new routes put up on the grit stone edges from 1970 onwards. In only three years he had redefined what was possible but in 1973 John Syrett's climbing career at the very top came to a tragic end. The climbing scene at the time was renowned for drinking, partying and recreational drug use. At one of the parties, John sliced through a tendon in his hand attempting to open a can of beer[134]

---

134 The ring pull had yet to be invented.

with a knife. In the years that followed he hit the bottle hard and suffered from depressive episodes. He was eventually found dead at the base of Malham Cove in 1985 and the coroner returned an open verdict[135].

One of the climbers John had inspired was Pete Livesey. Pete also had a sporting background having been a national standard schoolboy runner and a top level caver. One of his main climbing partners John Sheard said that,

"for Pete to apply the definition of 'rock climber' to himself, it had to include the unspoken prefix 'best'; anything else was playing around."

With that mind set and the application of training principles gained in athletics, Livesey had the natural qualifications to become one of the first of the new breed of climber and probably the best of his day.

Pete was one of the many who used to go to the Leeds Wall and spend a lot of time traversing but, whilst the others seemed to be getting as much fun from indoor climbing as outdoor, Livesey had other plans. As a result of his exploits on the crags, the upper limit of the grading system of climbing difficulty in the UK was pushed from E4 to E6 with the highest technical difficulty, previously 6a, being redefined as 6b. One of his most famous first ascents was *Right Wall* on Dinas Cromlech in 1974. This bold and committing E5 still sees off many contenders and today it is considered a rite of passage for any extreme rock climber. Even so, it was soloed within a decade by Phil Davidson in 1983!

Right Wall tackles the blank looking football-pitch-sized wall flanking the right hand side of Joe Brown's *Cenotaph Corner*. Untypically for its era, it did not follow an obvious

---

135 There is a fuller history of John Syrett at Footless Crow -

http://footlesscrow.blogspot.co.uk/2011/04/gritstone-visionary.html

line. Indeed on my first ever attempt to climb this route, I became hopelessly lost in a sea of rock and retreated beaten. Like Livesey, I turned to the climbing wall for a winter of training before a friend dragged me back up there for a second go. This time, physically and mentally better prepared and with a partner who had lapped the route many times, I set off.

To this day I cannot put myself into Livesey's mind as he created this work of route finding genius. Several meandering lines link two ledges with run-out climbing in between and today's gear does nothing to alleviate the problems. The crux occurs just above the final girdle ledge, where a sequence of 6a moves leads up to the 'porthole'. Here a dilemma must be faced. Stop to place a small wire and risk being too pumped to do the next section? Or commit to the next few moves without protection to bring a jug within reach? I chose to keep charging on. I ran out the rope for some 30ft and tried not to look down at the air I was likely to take. On reaching that jug the final difficulties were over and the view down the whole of *Right Wall* was amazing. I wondered for a second if Pete had taken a moment to look down at his masterpiece and whether he could ever have imagined that on busy days those wanting to repeat his route have to form a queue!

Hot on Livesey's heels was his own protégé and frequent partner, Ron Fawcett[136] who eventually took over from his mentor responsibility for driving the limits of possiblity relentlessly upwards. Ron put up his first new route in 1972 when he was only 15 years old. It was an E3 named *Mulatto Wall* in Malham Cove. Later he added an even greater line than *Right Wall* on Dinas Cromlech on

---

136 Ron Fawcett's book 'Ron Fawcett on Rock' is one of the great reads but his autobiography edited by Ed Douglas, 'Ron Fawcett: Rock Athlete' is possibly one of the best climbing books not to feature snow!

June 2nd 1979 when he climbed *Lord of the Flies*. The first ascent was filmed and, high on the route, facing another crux section, Ron's heartfelt

'Come on arms do your stuff'

was recorded in close-up for posterity. It has since become the climbing quote which is probably repeated more often than any other, usually with the quiet desperation reserved for prayers. At E6 and over 40 metres in height, *'Lord'* still has a fiery reputation but it too was eventually soloed by Dave Thomas in 1990.

A year after Fawcett's ascent of *Lord of the Flies,* a new piece of climbing equipment hit the market; the Boreal *Firé*, acclaimed as the first sticky rubber rock shoe. A belief popularly, but wrongly, held in climbing circles was that all rubber is sticky if it is warm enough but this was challenged by Boreal. Using a new formula to produce the rubber, their version was stickier at lower temperatures than EBs, the previous market leader. The instant popularity of the Firé was probably also boosted by a very badly timed business decision by the makers of EBs. In an effort to keep up with rising demands for their shoes, they changed the manufacturing process and used moulded rubber sole units. Production was increased but the boot did not grip as well and the advantage was inadvertently handed to the new competitor.

British climber John Redhead[137] was wearing *Firé* shoes on Gogarth, Anglesey's intimidating sea cliff crag, when he

---

137 Redhead has been described as the Yin to Fawcett's Yang. Fawcett was regarded as the model professional climber and sponsors' ambassador. Redhead was the wild child who partied as hard as he climbed. He and his contemporaries developed several bouldering areas in Wales on which to train for climbing.

made the first ascent of *The Bells, The Bells* in 1980. This slab route, unrelenting in terms of its steepness and difficulty, was almost impossible to protect and had been termed a 'chop route' since a fall would almost certainly be fatal. It was ultimately given the grade E7. Ridiculously bold and serious, Redhead's route represented a new level of technical difficulty but, more importantly, a breakthrough in what could be achieved if fear were banished and the mind focussed completely on the objective. Arguably, the barrier breached here for the first time was a mental rather than a physical one and this jaw dropping resetting of the limits spurred on training on vertical walls and brick edge traverses as climbers adapted to this style of climbing.

The E7 grade was the limit of traditional climbing in the UK for several years until Johnny Dawes singlehandedly exceeded it by creating several E8s and a couple of E9s. He put up what is probably still his most celebrated route in 1986, an E9 on Cloggy called *The Indian Face*. John Redhead had attempted it earlier and given it the name *Tormented Ejaculation,* placing a bolt at his high point. The bolt was soon removed and Johnny was free to make the first ascent of this extremely bold climb. Once again, this leap forward depended upon mind-set and self-control as well as climbing skill, the ability to focus the mind was at least as important as making the moves.

At about the same time, a new kind of climbing energy started to emerge, showing itself as a new type of sports climbing[138] demanding power and power endurance. Two of the earliest exponents, Ron Kauk and John Bachar, had been battling over the first ascent of one of the world's

---

138 Sport climbing is free climbing where bolts have been drilled into the rock to provide protection allowing the climber to concentrate solely making the moves.

most celebrated boulder problems, *Midnight Lightning* in Yosemite and it was Kauk who first climbed it in 1978. But Bachar was determined to make the boulders of Yosemite's Camp IV his own by showboating with a daily ascent of this benchmark V9 and following up with training on his famous elbow-exploding Bachar ladder[139]. Originally the route was thought to be impossible or, as Bachar explained using the words of a Hendrix song, the chance of it being climbed was as good as the chance of a lightning strike at midnight. So Bachar[140] drew a lightning bolt on the rock where it remains today[141], the pictograph having become a bouldering icon.

The earliest development of bouldering and sport climbing took place in France, Germany and Belgium. The levels of difficulty achieved by climbers who were freed from having to concentrate on placing gear, route finding or making sequences of unprotected moves rose quickly. And by 1983 this style of climbing was rapidly gaining popularity in the rest of the world, especially in the UK and the USA. The demands of this form of the sport required training methods to be adapted and many transformed space at home in cellars or sheds for training.

'Cellar boards' of plywood with a large selection of small holds on them are easily and cheaply made and installed. These allow fingers, arms, shoulders and core muscles to be worked hard while climbing. The dedicated are often delighted by their increased finger strength and

---

139 This is an inclined rope ladder for practising climbing using only handholds to work the shoulders and arms.

140 Link to Bachar's Story -

http://www.supertopo.com/climbing/thread.php?topic_id=396334

141 Although it was scrubbed off in 2012, but I suspect it is already replaced.

power. But many find the training itself becomes almost addictive and, done too intensively, it causes serious finger injuries.

A more extreme version, and as we will see even more likely to cause injuries, is the German Campus Board. Designed for footless training, the holds permit only the tips of the fingers to grip. The first was named when it was installed at the Campus Centre at the University in Nurnberg in 1988 by its designer Wolfgang Gullich. In 2007, the British Journal of Sports Medicine published a study which suggested use by youngsters should be avoided on finding x-ray evidence of permanent finger deformity in some competitive young climbers. In 2011, the UIAA and BMC followed suit with a warning that under-18s using campus boards regularly risk permanent damage to the growth plates in their fingers.

Wolfgang's training on the campus board was specifically focussed on preparation for an attempt on a new route in the Frankenjura where the hard, steep routes require immense finger strength and power, often requiring big moves to and from one or two finger pockets on alarmingly steep rock.

The Frankenjura also has a long history as a proving ground for free climbing. And it was there in the mid-1970s that Kurt Albert was improving his technique by trying not to conform to the local practice of using pegs to provide aid or a rest. After each climb, he painted a red cross over every peg he had not used except for protection. If he succeeded in climbing a route from the ground up without any falls or rests, he would mark it with a red dot, or 'Rotpunkt' in German. In doing so, Kurt coined the term and the ethic of redpointing, a key factor in the development of sports climbing a decade later. Since then the ethic of a climber rehearsing sections of a route for as long as necessary to make a successful ascent has produced a great rise in sport climbing standards. It has also been applied on the hardest trad climbs such as Johnny Dawes' *Indian Face*, where routes are tried on a top rope until the climber feels confident enough to dare to lead them.

Early in Wolfgang Gullich's training he was joined by British climber, Jerry Moffat, who said,
   "*I trained on* [the campus board] *stacks that winter and got dead strong. I went out and climbed 8b+* [5.14a] *straight away. I was doing them in a couple of tries.*"
   This grade was an incredible achievement for the time and Jerry believed quite rightly that,
   "*If the hard moves at the bottom of a route start to feel easy, you're going to be less pumped by the time you reach the top*".

Gullich would show this to be true and, through the use of his campus board and redpointing, he went on to define new limits in terms of power and power endurance. His 1984 route *Kamal im Rucken* was the world's first 8b, which he followed a year later with *Punks in the Gym* F8b+. A little over a year later, in 1987, he climbed the first F8c; *Wall Street*. British climber Ben Moon, also a training partner of Jerry Moffat, beat Gullich to the first 8c+ when he climbed *Hubble*. But it was Gullich who produced *Action Direct*, the first 9a, in 1991 on his home crag in the Frankenjura.

At the time relatively unnoticed, climbing legend Johnny Dawes had been steadily adding to a truly impressive list of achievements. These included developing one of the hardest slabs in the world in the Dinorwic slate quarries of Llanberis in North Wales. On this smooth surface he created an 8b+, *The Very Big and the Very Small* in 1990. Nearby is one of his earlier routes, the four pitches of *The Quarryman*. Put up in 1986, this became the more famous line having been recorded for posterity in the film *Stone Monkey*[142]. It was years before it was repeated but it was a project of Johnny's he called *Meltdown* which truly stood the test of time. On an early attempt in the 1980s, Johnny managed to link a sequence of moves that warranted F8c but, because he did not complete the route, this was never really acknowledged. It was not until 2012 that this project was finally climbed by James McHaffie. At F9a, it became the new hardest slab in the world and confirmed that Johnny had probably made one of the hardest climbing links of that time.

Wolfgang Gullich's contribution to the exponentially rapid rise of the hardest possible grade ended in 1992 with a tragic accident. Returning from doing a TV interview about his stunt work on the *Cliffhanger* movie, he crashed his sports car. In his friend's biography of him[143] is a clear account of his climbing philosophy and some unparallelled motivational and succinct quotes about training;

"The brain is the most important muscle for climbing."

"You don't go for a cup of coffee after climbing; rather, going out for coffee is part of climbing."

A personal favourite is;

"The hardest part of training is making the decision to start training at all."

Gullich did not restrict himself solely to bolted sport climbs. He made an unroped ascent of *Edge Lane* in the Peak District and then fell from the crux of a neighbouring

---

142 The film Stone Monkey is about Johnny Dawes and it captures his flamboyantly dynamic climbing style. It was one of the first climbing films to use the emerging technology of low cost videotape. The proliferation of this and then digital video in conjunction with home editing eventually led to the YouTube revolution of self broadcasting.

143 Tilmann Hepp, Wolgang Gullich: A Life in the Vertical, 1994.

line, *Master's Edge,* one of the hardest and boldest trad climbs in the UK. The result was a broken vertebra but three months later he was in Yosemite soloing the outrageous roof crack *Separate Reality* high above the valley floor.

Following the example of Gullich and others who translated training into spectacular achievement on the rock, more climbers began improvising their own training facilities. Clearly, this was a potential market and it was growing rapidly. In response to the demand, many sports centres in the UK managed to find some space and a wall to convert by embedding lumps of rock in the brickwork to create holds. But in 1991 the Foundry opened in Sheffield as the first purpose built climbing facility in the UK. Called a 'climbing wall', it was actually a huge room in which all the walls were artificial rock faces bristling with holds placed to create 'routes' of all levels of difficulty. Some were seriously overhanging, designed to mimic the types of climbs then being attempted by the very best exponents of the sport. Soon similar facilities sprang up and still spring up all over the country as an integral part of the growing leisure industry. These 'walls' have greatly increased the number of climbers and the levels of difficulty they achieve and indoor climbing has virtually become a sport in its own right.

The exponential nature of the growth in the numbers participating in climbing is illustrated by the membership records of the British Mountaineering Council. In 1980, 223 clubs and 3157 individual members were registered with the BMC. Although the number of club members and how many were also individual members were not recorded then, this gives an approximate baseline. In 1990, the number of clubs had risen to 270, representing 19 100 members and there were a further 6829 individual members making a total of 25 929. Another decade on, at the beginning of the millennium, this number had more than doubled to 52 023 members. Today it has grown by a further fifty percent to around 74 000 members and Climbing (rock climbing and mountaineering combined) is one of the top twenty sports in the UK and probably the world[144].

After an initial time lag, the increase in the number of purpose built climbing walls mirrored this pattern which proved that the growth and demand of this new market was potentially huge. And so it proved to be. In 1988, the BMC listed 40 walls of the early rudimentary type. As the nineties began, so did The Foundry and by 1995 the list had trebled to 122, practically all of them brand new, purpose built facilities since the old style walls had quickly become obsolete. This was remarkable because of the speed with which the technology was developed to construct wall panels and manufacture the bolt-on hand and foot holds so that routes could be designed, regularly changed and endlessly varied. A year later, this rapidly burgeoning industry had established an astonishing 169 climbing walls country wide and by 2003 there were 254. Now there are well over 300 walls accessible to the public and that figure does not include those in private use in schools, gyms and by the military.

Indoor climbing in this country received a further encouraging boost at that time when British climber, Simon Nadin, won the first ever World Climbing Championships in 1989. The existence of first class facilities in the UK enabled several of the rounds of subsequent World Championships to be held here from 1991 onwards.

---

144 Figures from the US estimate as many as 4 million people sport climbing in 2011.

It is hard to prove conclusively that the far greater opportunity to access climbing wall facilities directly caused the huge increase in the numbers of climbers. But the official BMC membership[145] figures strongly indicate that this is so, showing rapid growth coinciding with the proliferation of climbing walls even without the many climbers who are not members of clubs or the BMC. This is not a 'smoking gun' connection of course but there has been no other factor as powerfully instrumental. We have reached a point where, a single generation after it was a rare thing to train on a wall to improve climbing fitness, it is now unusual to meet a climber whose skills are not regularly honed at the local wall. That the vast majority of climbers now have access to a climbing wall is taken for granted these days. My next contention is also unsupported by hard data but it seems that most climbers under the age of thirty were introduced to the sport not as young adults at a distant crag but as children at their local wall by their school, youth group, holiday play scheme or a friend's birthday party. No wonder the number of new climbers continues to grow!

Many of the climbers who have excelled indoors when young, just like Syrett, have then gone on to make an impressive impact outdoors. Two climbers spring to mind; Ben Bransby and Leo Houlding. Back in the 1990s they competed in the first indoor climbing comps and are now both very accomplished rock climbers, big wallers and alpine mountaineers. They belong to a brave new breed of wall rats who have taken the strength, stamina, power and technique built on indoor walls and applied them to climbing outdoors. Nevertheless, the transition from indoors to outdoors can lead to problems.

---

145 See page 6 for the graph on BMC membership from 1991 to 2011 -
http://www.thebmc.co.uk/media/files/AGM/BMC%20Annual%20Repor
t%202011.pdf

Climbers who learn indoors become very physically fit but they often find that there are aspects of outdoor climbing that they have not mastered. The ability to read the rock for hand and foot holds is a key example. Knowing how to place protection and establish anchors to secure themselves to the rock at belays are others. The initial lack of these skills in those who make the move from indoor to outdoor climbing has arguably led to the growth in sports climbing. On these sports routes, which are equipped with bolts, the skills required are much more akin to those developed on a wall. The last 10 years have seen a 10% increase in both sport climbing and bouldering in the UK, mostly at the cost of traditional climbing. The importance of training to make the transition from indoor to outdoor climbing is widely recognised to the extent that Sport England has provided some additional funding for courses.

During the same year that the Foundry first welcomed climbers, elsewhere the lid of a technological Pandora's box was prised open and the legacy of that action has touched everyone on the planet. On Christmas Day 1991, British scientist Tim Bernes-Lees effectively switched on the world wide web. He developed it as a piece of software for use on computers linked by a phone line so that the scientists he worked with at the European nuclear research establishment, CERN, could share information.

As ever, this breakthrough was the result of the creative use of existing ideas because computers had already been connected in networks. In fact, scientist J.C.R Licklider foresaw the internet back in 1962 as a symbiosis of humans and computers in a paper in which he described.....
"a *network of such* [computers]*, connected to one another by wide-band communication lines* [to provide] *the functions of*

present-day libraries together with anticipated advances in information storage and retrieval and [other] *symbiotic functions."*

Within five years an embryonic ARPANET[146] was being trialed for the first time with two connected computers on either side of the United States. Telling the story, one of the scientists said,

"We set up a telephone connection between us and the guys at SRI ... We typed the L and we asked on the phone,

"Do you see the L?"

"Yes, we see the L," came the response.

"We typed the O, and we asked, "Do you see the O."

"Yes, we see the O."

"Then we typed the G, and the system crashed ...Yet a revolution had begun."

From those humble beginnings, various computer networks grew however each was unique and to a certain extent platform dependent. In short, communication was possible within but not between networks. When setting out his proposal for a world wide web, Tim Bernes-Lee recognised that for it to succeed it needed to meet the following criteria:

An information system must be able to record random associations between any arbitrary objects, unlike most database systems;

If two sets of users started to use the system independently, to make a link from one system to another should be an incremental effort, not requiring unscalable operations such as the merging of link databases.

Any attempt to constrain users as a whole to the use of particular languages or operating systems was always doomed to failure;

Information must be available on all platforms, including future

---

146 This was a precursor to the internet; a large, wide-area network created by (the United States Defence) Advanced Research Project Agency.

ones;

Any attempt to constrain the mental model users have of data into a given pattern was always doomed to failure;

If information within an organization is to be accurately represented in the system, entering or correcting it must be trivial for the person directly knowledgeable.

These criteria actually defined the practical basis that made the internet possible. Most importantly though, Tim Bernes-Lee also ensured that the Internet was licence and royalty free. The open source ethos he created is embodied in the work he still carries out as the Director of the World Wide Web Consortium (W3C), responsible for maintaining web standards and promoting interoperable web technologies. Tim also made a surprise appearance at the London 2012 Olympics where he sent a tweet to the stadium and the world simply saying,

"This is for Everyone."

Initially regarded like something out of Orwell's '1984', the impact of the web could only be imagined then. Now, as predicted, the web has become omnipresent throughout the developed world. Entire online communities have been built using Tim's framework and software developed using W3C guidelines. With the continued development of free open source data, the internet already lives up to one of its other names, 'the information superhighway'. If we did not already take for granted our ability to track down and access so much information instantly, we would be better able to appreciate the miraculous power the internet confers on us. This book would certainly have been much harder to research without the likes of Google and the Gutenberg Project scanning and posting online books outside their copyright.

As with every other aspect of our lives, the effect of the internet on our passion for climbing has been inescapable.

Before the 1990s, the print media had the monopoly on the information we climbers could access. But suddenly, websites dedicated to our sport appeared and we could read next month's climbing magazine before it went to print because of the inherent lag time in designing layouts and gathering stories. Similarly, there has been an explosion in the amount of information available on training for climbing. Now, articles, film clips and even web-based applications[147] can help those who want to research their own training.

In the last 10 years, the rapid take up of what has been dubbed Web 2.0 has spurred the web to a new level. This is the user generated content of online forums, wikis, blogs and the social media. The method of news delivery has redefined the sources of that news. For the first time, the people who are the subject of the news have the opportunity to report it themselves. In climbing, those who are making the hard ascents write their own news on their blogs. Posts that capture the imagination of their public spread like wild fire across the social media. This was vividly illustrated in the autumn of 2011, when two young British climbers went to the States to take on the off-width crack climbs. So called because they are an awkward width to climb and difficult to protect, these routes are renowned for needing highly specialist skills. The blog the pair kept, The Wide Boyz, had an estimated 11 000 hits in the first two weeks and 'went viral' as other climbers joined in, sharing their stories and passing judgement by blogging on their own feats of off-width slot climbing.

---

147 One such web based application resides at

http://iCoachClimbing.com Its premise is to automate ways to identify

weaknesses and training for those specific climbing skills. It was

programmed by the author of this book as a hobby.

It is important to remember that when the internet started in 1991, a computer was as big as a suitcase, had a1Gb hard drive and ran at 100 mhz. My iPhone has more processing power and memory than that today and it fits in my pocket. With faster processing and the speed of the world wide data networks the internet is constantly evolving and, most importantly of all for instant news distribution, it can be accessed from almost inaccessible places; base camp, the bivvi ledge, the belay stance or the summit.

These days the climbing community not only has immediate notification of new achievements as they happen but websites have become places where detailed information about routes, the 'beta', is revealed. They are sources of training information and, more recently, they have started to replace the new routes books. Wiki[148] sites, open to all contributors, have taken over as the way to share the latest routes. The arrival of digital video recording provides the means to film and edit exploits and achievements on home PCs and publish them on vimeo and youtube. This 'broadcast yourself' revolution has been wholeheartedly embraced by climbers and many make their news, information and opinions available to the rest of the world.

The speed with which information is shared has had as profound an effect on climbing as on every other aspect of our lives. The importance of access to basic information became obvious when the very first climbing guide books

---

148 Wiki sites contain lots of information generated by its users. In the UK the first came about when the guidebook for Gogarth went out of print and I was so frustrated about the situation I set up a site. It was followed shortly afterwards by Slate, Tremadog, North Wales Limestone and Welsh Winter Climbs wiki sites. http://gogarth.wetpaint.com

were published almost a century ago. Simply being able to locate crags and routes encouraged everyone, not just those 'in the know', to go and attempt them. The same is equally true now but it happens instantaneously and average climbers are spurred on by being able to track what the elite are making possible. The effect has been to drive the average grade achieved by the majority ever upwards.

Faster and more powerful computers were the key to another important development; they permitted manufacturers to design and engineer lighter, more user friendly equipment over a much shorter time span. The weight of each item of equipment limits the number of pieces which can be carried on a climb. On a route, a climber has a 'rack' of gear clipped to loops on the harness or on a bandolier strap across the shoulder. The rack must provide a choice of sizes and shapes to fit the fissures offered by that particular type of rock at short enough intervals for safety. Clearly, a case of more being more here!

The rapidly evolving design of ever lighter equipment significantly increases the size of the rack we can carry. It is not uncommon now to see a climber starting up an adventurous sea cliff or big wall with at least a complete set of camming devices, two sets of nuts on wire, a selection of the tiny nuts on wire called micros and more than 14 of the short slings with a karabiner at each end known as quickdraws. With a greater selection of superior kit for no extra weight, all climbers have been able to attempt increasingly harder routes. As could have been predicted, this boosted the general standard still further.

At the forefront of these developments was DMM, a major manufacturing company founded in 1981 with the single objective of making the best climbing equipment at the best prices. The team at DMM was as cunning at strategy as they were brilliant at design and the piece of equipment that put them on the map was the Mamba. A sports climbing quickdraw that could be clipped quickly and efficiently, it worked well on hard redpoints and was the world leader in its functionality. The Mamba used a lightweight sling to link a pair of karabiners which were the first ever to be made by hot forging aluminium. By reintroducing this process, previously used only on steel, DMM could create shapes which were aesthetically pleasing, more functional and lighter than all of the competition. Whilst others continued to make karabiners by bending 10mm thick round bars of aluminium to shape, DMM were squeezing the metal to where it was needed and removing it from where it was not.

The company's reputation as innovators was assured when they went on to redesign the ice axe. DMM designers took the concept of the 'bent shafted' ice axe produced by Grivel in 1986 and replaced the kink in the shaft with a smooth curve. The head of the axe was a beautifully sculpted shape that only hot forging could produce and, with the pick and adze attached, the Predator came into being. It was the first and, for a long time, the only one of its kind in production. So sinister looking was this 'weapon', it appeared in a mainstream thriller as the murder weapon.

The axe was a game changer in ice climbing. The crushed knuckles caused by climbing vertical ice with a traditional straight shafted axe were a thing of the past. But it also changed the ergonomics of using an ice axe. It was more natural to hold and penetrated the ice to give a secure placement with far less effort. The DMM sales reps after the Predator came out, Neil Gresham and Tim Emmett, had entered the first ever Ice Climbing World Cup and they spent as much time in the tool room trying to tweak the design for this as they did out on the road selling the equipment. On the ultra-steep and over-hanging ice artificially created for competition, axes cannot be attached by leashes to the wrists because, once placed in the ice, they will be needed as interchangeable holds for either hand. The new wave of steep leashless climbing on mixed ice and rock developed and so did the design of the axes and more than one or two prototypes made it to the comps. But DMM's market was to equip the classic challenges of British mixed winter climbing. And the Grivel and Petzl companies have seemed to draw ahead in the arena of competition climbs and the upside down routes of Europe and America in recent years. However, it must be said that some of these designs, notably the Petzl Nomic, have possibly gone too far. I am sure that more than one pair of climbers has got to the top of Aonach Mor and other winter descent gullies and looked down mystified at how to cut a snow bollard to abseil from without an adze.

A further revolution for the modern ice climber was the monopoint crampon produced at around the same time by both Grivel and Charlet-Moser. With only a single, very strong, forward facing point which could be placed on a small hold or driven securely into ice, these are the crampons of choice on difficult rock and ice routes. Then DMM made the Terminator monopoint crampons totally asymmetrical which added another innovation to the mix. But possibly the most creative design tweak was seen at the Ice Climbing World Cup when climbers simply started bolting crampons directly to their rock boots, adding an aggressive heel spur so that they could hang upside down like bats. Many people saw this as a form of cheating and 'spurred' versus 'spurless' ascents were made of existing routes. But, spurs were here to stay after the climbers equipped to use their heels on steeper mixed ground led a meteoric rise in standards.

A further ground breaking piece of winter equipment was developed by Black Diamond; the express ice screw. Essentially like conventional screws, these are driven into the ice at intervals and the rope is clipped to them for protection. But placing one took a nerve wracking two minutes of fighting with leashes, gravity and the screw itself. It was at best reluctant to go into the ice and often the axe, desperately needed for its main function (stopping one falling to one's death), had to be used instead to get enough leverage to rotate the screw. Then Black Diamond put a simple handle on one and an ice screw can now be placed in under 30 seconds. I am sure many ice climbers would love to shake the hand of the person who made that possible.

Meanwhile, the drive for the perfect karabiner has continued and DMM has been at the forefront by improving the existing technology and making it their own. Throughout the late nineties and the early years of this century, the Karabiner Wars have raged. Every year, DMM, Camp, Black Diamond, Petzl and Wild Country fought to be known as the producer of "The Lightest Snapgate Karabiner in the World". It seemed that no sooner had advertisements gone to print than they became obsolete with the launch of another 'world-beater'. As the karabiners got lighter they also got smaller. Eventually, obsessed with the quest for lightness, some manufacturers forgot about function. With a few notable exceptions, DMM's lightest karabiner being one, some others are so small they look like novelty toys or key rings. Their technical specifications assure us that we can use them for climbing but unfortunately the size of the human hand and the diameter of even our thinnest ropes makes that difficult.

One piece of DMM kit is praised by those who find it

useful although it is not given the same acclaim as their best known products. But the story behind it is intriguing and illustrates the process that often precedes innovation. Picture the DMM design team and sales staff sitting round a table trying to come up with the next 'big idea'. Spread out on the table is the equipment a climber would take on a route and the question is posed "What is the heaviest thing on the rack?" The hope was that technical adjustment would shave off grams here and there. Then someone piped up "Well, the rope is the heaviest thing on the rack." Whilst not obviously helpful, the observation was undeniably true and it did open up the debate.

Besides making a rope thinner and therefore lighter, how else can its weight be reduced? The answer was to lessen the drag caused by friction as the rope meanders from one piece of protection to the next, a common problem especially on the traditional routes of the UK. Whereas the weight of the rope is largely unavoidable, friction in a system can be reduced by making it more efficient. This proved to be a 'light bulb' moment. Pulleys reduce friction so they put a small pulley at the base of a karabiner. Tests followed at the local climbing wall watched incidentally by me and others who happened to be there. A route was climbed and the rope was clipped into the alternate bolts from two adjacent routes. The resulting zigzag soon produced so much rope drag that the climber could hardly move. Then they did the same using the prototype 'pulley' karabiner and the reduction in resistance was instantly noticeable. And that is how the revolver karabiner came to be.

This was not the end of the story for one of DMM's business partners on the project. Beginning his working day by opening the doors of his establishment at 9am, he was surprised when a heavily armed Police Anti-terrorism unit stormed through them. From the position he had assumed seconds later face down on the floor, he gathered from what the police were saying that they were interested in his recent phone calls to DMM to discuss the 'barrels' for the 'revolver' and the 'trigger' mechanism for cams his company was making for them. Too many weapons related terms had activated an automatic listening system. Big Brother alerted a keen police officer and the SWAT team were there before you could say "Nine eleven".

It seems then that the climbers of today have reached a point where they are armed with all the training facilities, information and high tech kit they could need to face any challenge they choose. So I have kept the promise I made at the outset of this book to track key advances made by the human race through the ages and especially how they have impacted on climbing. I have no doubt failed to include innovations, people and achievements which should have appeared. But in these chapters I have covered those I think are the most important to the sport which is my passion. To be honest, others have been included simply because I hope you find them as interesting as I do. A complete chronicle of events is way beyond the scope of this book but I point you at some of the very many excellent sources of information out there, both in published books and free content on the internet. If, amongst all the jumbled pieces of that magnificently complex and colourful jigsaw that is our culture, science and technology, I have supplied you with some of the pieces with the straight sides and maybe a corner or two, then job done!

To conclude, I feel obliged, in spite of risking being even more incomplete, to pass on something that will inevitably be out of date by the time you read this; my predictions of some future trends. These trends feature sciences that have come into being during the lifetimes of most of us. They are communications technology, materials science and genetics.

In every field of research, the skills of computer scientists are needed to design applications to deal with astronomically large amounts of data. But many of the skills that were the exclusive preserve of experts a decade ago are now within the power of the ordinarily computer literate person. The resultant sharing of information makes an infinite pool of collective knowledge available to us and we 'ordinary' folk are only just beginning to explore how we choose to use it.

The sharing of knowledge brought about by computers has already had a great impact on climbing. In 2010, an attempt to take the wiki sites a stage further by making an online guidebook led to the next generation of guides in the form of an application where all the climbing areas, crags, topo diagrams and routes are stored as a database on your smart phone. It enables routes to be searched by grade, name, first ascentionists, stars, crag or proximity. I was fortunate enough to be part of that initial movement and Steve Golley, the real brains behind the idea, and I produced the first full scale selective guide to one of the most popular climbing areas in the UK, North Wales. At the moment, the print media are still ahead of us but we have made the crucial first steps and will be constantly pushing and updating the database as more people get pocket computers. In the near future I see a boom in the provision of handy apps where text, pictures and video will be combined as an interactive ebook in the form of an instructional climbing manual. Even a coach that is essentially a set of computer code, may well become one of the tools we use to learn to climb and to improve.

Newly developed materials show great promise for the benefit of all humankind of course. But the modern climber's obsession is with the weight of the gear that has to be carried versus its functionality. There has been talk of a carbon fibre karabiner[149] but problems are anticipated because early versions of the carbon fibre shafted ice axes available have tended to snap. Also at present, even the lightest aluminium 'krabs' are stronger than their carbon fibre counterparts. For now, the possible safety compromises and lack of durability of the carbon fibre versions are unjustifiable for the small weight saving.

Unsurprisingly, there is a keen interest in potential weight savings amongst those who haul large amounts of gear vertically upwards, sometimes for days, to climb the big walls. Innovative manufacturers, A5, split from their parent company, the North Face, to make gear exclusively for big wall climbing. They have made a prototype carbon-fibre version of the 'portaledge' needed as a refuge from the weather, a sleeping platform and a gear stash. They achieved a significant weight saving of 2 kilos but the associated quadrupling in cost makes it economically unviable for the time being.

The remarkable molecular properties of carbon have been destined to be hugely important since a team at Rice University in Houston discovered carbon 'Bucky balls' in 1985. These molecules are named after Buckminster Fuller because they resemble the geodesic dome structure he invented. His pattern of hexagons and pentagons linked to make self-supporting spherical surfaces is now frequently seen in tent and roof designs, the Eden Project being a notable example. Since then, discrete tubes of carbon with a similar structure, each topped with a half a Bucky ball, have been grown. In 2004, a 4 cm long, single-walled nanotube was made which showed the immense strength of carbon in this form. Eventually, it may transform

---

149 Website on the carbon fibre karabiner.

http://www.crabdev.co.uk/comp%20introduction.htm

textiles as radically as nylon once did. Imagine ropes and slings made from this stuff! But the amazing nanotube already has many other potential applications not the least of these being that it can work in electrical circuits, functioning not just as wiring but also as memory circuits. This is a technology which is just beginning but it can confidently be predicted that it will feature in our future in the next few years.

Another apparently miraculous material, seemingly brought to us directly from the realms of science fiction, is a sticky tape with no actual adhesive which will stick to glass. It uses the same principle as a gecko's feet[150]. Thousands of closely bunched hairs with flat, almost sucker-like ends, hold the tape (and indeed the gecko's foot it imitates) in place using the Van der Waals force. This is the tiny force between atomic structures. But, applied as many times as there are atoms, that is a lot of force. In a demonstration of its holding power, a sheet of the material of just under a square foot in size was placed on a piece of Perspex mounted to a ceiling and a brave person could hang from it. Now, I will admit that when I first read about this material, I did fantasise for a while about the routes I could climb if I had gloves and shoes made from it. Inevitably, the day will come when applications are found for it in climbing and the discussions on how we adapt the ethos of our sport to accept this particular technology will be fascinating.

Personally, I find the likely future effects of one area of science quite alarming and that is genetic engineering. Examples which have fired my imagination include the goat with altered DNA whose milk produces the same protein found in spiders' silk. This can be spun into long

---

150 A video about the Gecko hair technology -

http://www.youtube.com/watch?v=gzm7yD-JuyM

filaments which could in the future be transplanted into humans as tendon grafts. Another is the genetically modified bacterium which consumes sugar and excretes diesel oil. It may solve the problem of dwindling fossil fuel supplies whilst simultaneously saving the Western world from obesity and type two diabetes. It may also justify the faith of the Ford car executive who, when asked about the oil crisis, simply said, *'The Stone Age didn't end because we ran out of stones.'*

Science may already be on the verge of redirecting evolution. A transgenic super mouse[151] has been created. With DNA altered to produce more muscle fibre, this mouse could run further, live longer and have more sex than other mice. Exciting stuff? Well, maybe. Modern society has mixed feelings about genetic experimentation on humans so the ethics are muddled to say the least and legislation, rules and guidelines always follow a step or two behind the science. When it is carried out for medical reasons such as the DNA profiling of cancers to choose targeted medication, we are all for it. But I wonder what our response will be when the time comes that the same experiment is tried to enhance performance in sport[152].

In previous chapters I have outlined some of the technological advances which have brought the human race to this point in its development. The most recent give us clues to our future and I have briefly speculated on what these might be. I find that I have also illustrated the

---

151 A video of the mouse, be warned there is a dissection at the end.

http://www.youtube.com/watch?v=WdA89Cps3sc

152 Sadly, at the London 2012 Olympics, a Chinese athlete was nearly accused of doping despite lack of evidence after knocking several seconds off her personal best. An American who did the same thing raised no such concerns. There were rumours of genetic doping though.

irony that climbing, the sport many of us love as an escape from a busy world, has at every point in its history been shaped by the culture, science and technology of that world. Fortunate to have visited cliffs in many countries to repeat famous historic routes, I am always awed to be using the same holds that many climbers have used before me and many more will use afterwards. I always wonder how the world was at the time the first ascentionists were practising their art on that rocky canvas.

For as long as we live on this planet, climbers will be struggling upwards against gravity. Which genre of the sport we choose is up to us. How much of a struggle we want to make it and how much we want to rely on help from technology is up to us too. The achievements of the past make these choices possible. Now we all climb on our own terms, adapting our philosophy for our own times. But the history of climbing is written and we can judge our own efforts against those benchmarks of the past.

The best thing about the future, is that it is unwritten. Whilst trying to predict it is an uncertain business, there are some givens. The chief of these is that we humans will always respond to this planet and beyond with a readiness to explore and invent which, I hope I have convinced you, have driven our every achievement since we first stood upright and walked.

ABOUT THE AUTHOR

Mark is a mountaineering instructor and author based in North Wales. He spends most of his time either teaching people to climb or helping train other mountain instructors. When not working or writing mark spends his time rock climbing on the many classic sea and mountain cliffs of Snowdonia. You can keep up to date on what he is up to via his long running blog lifeinthevertical.co.uk.

If you'd like to enjoy the mountains and cliffs of Wales with him then you can see the courses he offers at snowdoniamountainguides.com.

Mark's other books include:
- Effective Coaching: The Coaching Process for Climbing Instructors.
- A Mountaineers Guide to Avalanches
- How to Climb Harder – Pesda Press
- North Wales Climbs - Rockfax

Marks other website include:
- Icoachclimbing.com
- Verticallife.co.uk
- Climbingcoaches.co.uk

Made in the USA
Lexington, KY
06 December 2013